W9-BEC-194

The Academy Classics

THE MAGIC SPEAR

COMPILED BY

MARY McSKIMMON

PRINCIPAL OF THE PIERCE SCHOOL
BROOKLINE, MASSACHUSETTS

AND

VIRGINIA LYNCH

INSTRUCTOR IN EXTENSION
COLUMBIA UNIVERSITY

ALLYN AND BACON

| BOSTON | NEW YORK | CHICAGO |
| ATLANTA | SAN FRANCISCO | DALLAS |

Norwood Press
J. S. Cushing Co. — Berwick & Smith Co.
Norwood, Mass., U.S.A.

Mother had to meet her unwelcome guests supported only by her young children. (*A Pioneer Girl*)

PREFACE

The Magic Spear, whose title was suggested by Kipling's poem, *The Hour of the Angel*, is a collection of readings from both contemporary literature and the traditional classics. It includes biographical sketches, short stories, informal essays, and a one-act play. Such authors as James M. Barrie, Henry van Dyke, Thomas Nelson Page, Michael Pupin, Stewart Edward White, Selma Lagerlöf, Charles Dickens, George Meredith, are listed in the table of contents.

The Magic Spear is a literature textbook, whose aim is to provide readers of junior high school age with pleasant and profitable reading. However, it is more than a literature textbook. The selections included have been chosen because of their bearing on some aspect of character education. Many of the selections set forth with dramatic intensity critical situations that demand an ethical choice — situations that serve as the touch of Ithuriel's spear, revealing "unbacked competence and dower of judgment."

These dramatic moments in actual and fictitious lives, involving as they do significant crises, make a strong appeal to young people, who are profoundly concerned with shaping their philosophy of life. The exploratory attitude toward questions of ethics, conduct, vocations, and intellectual interests characterizes the junior high

iii

Preface

school age, the keenest interest being probably in matters of ethical conduct.

The text includes questions and topics for study, to insure correct interpretations of the selections and to provide materials that will provoke fruitful classroom discussion. A selected list of books suggests further reading in a field where the individual is constantly called on to test his ability to meet life situations and realize his success or unworthiness.

Special effort has been made to avoid preaching or moralizing, the selections being allowed to speak for themselves.

The text fits easily into representative courses of study in literature. It also meets the requirements of courses in character education, first getting the reader's attention by the appealing quality of the selections, and second, provoking thoughtful discussion of ethical and moral problems.

The illustrations by Joan Esley illuminate the text and make it attractive to young readers.

M. McS.
V. L.

CONTENTS

V

Contents

ILLUSTRATIONS

Illustrations

THE MAGIC SPEAR

The Hour of the Angel

RUDYARD KIPLING

Sooner or late — in earnest or in jest —
  (But the stakes are no jest) Ithuriel's Hour
Will spring on us, for the first time, the test
  Of our sole unbacked competence and power
  Up to the limit of our years and dower
Of judgment — or beyond. But here we have
Prepared long since our garland or our grave.
  For, at that hour, the sum of all our past,
  Act, habit, thought, and passion shall be cast
  In one addition, be it more or less,
  And as that reading runs so shall we do;
  Meeting, astounded, victory at the last,
  Or, first, and last, our own unworthiness.
And none can change us though they die to save!

Reprinted from *Land and Sea Stories for Boys and Girls* by permission of the author and Doubleday, Page & Co.

Ithuriel was that archangel whose spear had the magic property of showing every one exactly and truthfully what he was.

SILVER WINGS

Raoul Fauconnier Whitfield

HE was no longer Cadet Barry Lewis. Sam Browne belt, gold shoulder bars — and silver wings! He had dreamed of the day when he would wear them — these silver wings. They symbolized hours of desperate mental effort, minutes of skill and work 5 in the air. Ground work and air work, application and courage — all had contributed to this hour. He was no longer a cadet. Lieutenant Barry Lewis — a flying officer! The goal had been attained. 10

Coming out from the adjutant's office, into the nasty blow of a Texas norther, he had a broad grin on his lean, browned face. His eyes sparkled and he walked more erectly than ever. An enlisted man, a member of the ground crew outfits, snapped 15 up a salute — and Barry returned it with a thrill running through his entire body. His first salute!

His pride was pardonable. He had been through a great deal, had fought many battles with himself

Reprinted by courtesy of *Boys' Life*, published by the Boy Scouts of America.

before he had been eligible to wear the silver wings on the olive drab of his uniform. There had been times when failure seemed a certainty, success far beyond his reach. It had been a tough battle —
5 all of the way. And he had won.

He reached the corner of the barracks building in which he had been quartered. He would move his few things over to the officers' barracks now. Life would be different. The wings made a change;
10 the barriers were down now. He was *actually* a flyer!

Suddenly the smile left his face. His eyes met those of Cadet Bert Reade. And Cadet Reade's brown eyes held a peculiar expression, one half of
15 amusement, half of disgust. There was no doubt about the expression — or its meaning.

Lieutenant Barry Lewis pulled up sharply. His own gray eyes bored into those of the other man. A salute was due, and that was what he was waiting
20 to receive. Instead, Cadet Reade laughed. It was a nasty laugh. Then, without a word, leaving Barry standing in the barrack's path, rigid and slightly pale, the cadet turned away, rounded the corner of the long, white building — and was
25 gone.

For several seconds Lieutenant Lewis stood motionless. He had been in Cadet Reade's class in Ground School. He had even coached the other man in gunnery work, in aërial observation work.

4

He had noted the change. Now, because Cadet Reade had been dropped back a few grades, and was consequently outranked by Barry, he had failed to play the game as a soldier should play it. He had refused to recognize Barry as an officer should be recognized.

Barry Lewis relaxed suddenly. His fingers unclenched, his eyes became softer in expression. He liked Bert Reade very much. They had been real pals. But Bert was a cadet — and he was an officer. He had won the right to be an officer. He smiled grimly. When he entered the barracks and the other cadets sprang to their feet, he shouted an almost gay "At ease!"

But twenty minutes later he had reported Cadet Bert Reade for failure to salute an officer. And it was not such a minor infraction of the code — because, as Barry had stated in his report, it had been done deliberately. Colonel Hastings read the report, and was puzzled. He sent for Cadet Reade, talked with him. After which he confined the cadet to camp for ten days. For Barry was an officer — and wore the silver wings.

There was considerable talk in the cadet barracks. The cadets could not quite understand the affair. Barry had joked with them, had been the same as ever. The silver wings, the majority of them felt, had not given him a big head. He was a good scout. They told Cadet Reade as much.

But he was too bitter to listen to their words. Disappointment had caused him to laugh at his comrade, when he had first seen him wearing the silver wings. He had been ashamed, had hated himself for that sneering laugh, almost immediately. That was why he had turned away.

But Barry had reported him! That was the thing that hurt. Ten days of camp confinement — because Barry had reported him! It seemed so small. Even smaller than his laugh, and his failure to salute. It bred in Cadet Reade a hatred that he could not down.

Two days later he met Barry on the flying field. He saluted, with cold eyes and an expressionless face. Barry returned his salute in a similar manner. And then Cadet Reade got a little surprise.

"Cadet Reade — you are to go up above for final stunts with me." Barry's tone was like ice. "I'll tell you what I want you to do when we get up above. Lieutenant Mannfret is ill — I am taking his place. Try not to freeze on the controls."

Bert tensed at Barry's last words. They were insulting. With an effort he checked the words which wanted to come from between his lips. He got himself under control, smiled grimly.

"Very well, *sir!*" he said slowly, and moved toward the ship nearest the lieutenant.

As he climbed into the front cockpit, after strapping on his 'chute, there was a bitter smile on his

6

face. Barry Lewis was to give him his final instruction in stunting. *Lieutenant* Barry Lewis was to make the air safe for him — while he practiced making the air safe for himself! Within a week *he* would be an officer, unless something unforeseen 5 occurred — and yet now he must take instructions

" Cadet Reade — you are to go up above for final stunts with me."

from the man who had treated him like a child, from the man who had reported him! Because Barry Lewis was wearing the silver wings he had taken advantage —   10

"Ready, Cadet?" Barry's voice, sounding above the low roar of the Curtiss two-seater's engine, interrupted his thoughts.

"Yes, sir!" he replied, and the two-seater rolled

forward, handled finely under the practiced hands of Lieutenant Barry Lewis.

They got into the air, and the ship commenced a slow but steady climb for altitude in which to per-
5 form stunts. It was probably to be Cadet Reade's last flight — he should have been slightly excited at the thought. His last flight before getting the wings he had worked so hard to win! But he was not in the least excited. He sat rigidly in the front
10 cockpit — the place of the cadet when an officer was riding with him. There was sullenness within him — and hatred.

"Silver wings!" he muttered to himself as the Curtiss training ship climbed upward. "Taking
15 an instructor's place. Thinks he's about the greatest flyer in the world! Guess he's forgotten all about the time I worked with him all night on rigging and wireless code."

But Cadet Reade was wrong on that point.
20 Lieutenant Barry Lewis, climbing the ship from the rear cockpit, handling the joy stick and rudder with a calm skill, had *not* forgotten that time. He was thinking of it as the Curtiss reached an altitude of three thousand feet. With any other cadet as a
25 student passenger the sense of responsibility would have pleased, thrilled Barry. But with Bert Reade in the front cockpit he felt only a dull hurt. Bert had refused to recognize him — until punished. He had sneered at the silver wings.

8

Silver Wings

The Curtiss climbed on up into the cloudless sky — bearing two human beings as passengers. And both of them were thinking of other things than the job to be done. Which is not good — in the air.

At five thousand feet Barry Lewis rattled the joy stick violently, cut the engine, and shouted to the cadet in the front cockpit.

"Take the controls, Cadet! Keep her at this altitude, or within five hundred feet of it. Do figure-eights and shallow spirals until I tell you to stop."

Bert Reade made no reply. Anger was surging within him. Figure-eights and spirals were not exactly stunts. He had finished with that sort of thing weeks ago. He believed that Barry was simply trying to mock him — making him do childish stuff. Childish for the finished flyer, at least.

And again the cadet was wrong. He did not know that Captain Bracket, officer in charge of flying, was on the field and watching the two-seater in which he and Barry were flying. But Barry knew it, and because he guessed the state of Bert Reade's mind he had decided to give him a chance to feel the ship out in simple maneuvers.

Bert flew the two-seater sloppily. His execution was not bad, could not be detected from the ground. But Barry, riding behind the cadet, could feel every motion of the plane. The air was bumpy; it was early in the afternoon and the day was hot.

9

Barry rapped sharply on the side of the fuselage. It was a dual-control plane; he cut the engine, and nosed the ship down, taking the stick away from the cadet with a sharp jerk.

5 "Make your execution smoother!" he snapped. "She's slipping on the banks. Do a few more figure-eights, then go into some spins and loops — and keep her above three thousand."

He felt the joy stick jerked away from his fingers 10 with a real savageness as Bert Reade took control from the front cockpit. The figure-eights that followed were smoother — and yet he felt that the cadet could have made them smoother yet — had he wanted to fly at his best. There had never 15 been anything poor about Bert's flying. It was his class work that had kept him a cadet while Barry had been made an officer.

Suddenly the nose of the ship went down. Barry felt the sharp kick of the rudder that sent the 20 Curtiss into a swift spin. Downward the two-seater plunged, whirling like a top. She came out of it in a rush, and for a second the controls were in neutral. She plunged toward the earth — not spinning.

25 "Pull her out!" Barry shouted, but the ship continued to drop toward the field below. The wind was screaming through her wires, shrilling in the rigging.

"Pull her up!" Barry shouted for the second

10

time, and she came out of the dive with a rush.
The engine roared; Bert zoomed her straight to the
skies, gaining altitude on the momentum of the
plunge downward.

Lieutenant Barry Lewis's lips were set in a tight 5
line. He had not instructed the cadet to zoom
her. There was a second of indecision, in which
he contemplated taking control away from the man
in the front cockpit and bringing the plane to the
field. If he reported disobedience in the air, it 10
would go hard with Bert.

He dismissed the thought with a swift shame that
he had contemplated it. The Curtiss had been
leveled off. Bert was flying toward the center of
the field again. 15

"Turn her over!" Barry ordered sharply. "Put
her over in about five loops — and let her fall out
of the last one. Then pick her out of the spin —
and make a dead-engine landing. That's all."

The helmeted head of the man in the front cock- 20
pit jerked downward and back again in a brief nod.
The engine had been throttled down somewhat, and
it roared in full voice now.

Suddenly the nose of the ship went down, but the
engine was not cut. It continued to roar as loudly 25
as ever. Bert Reade was getting speed for the
upward zoom of the first loop.

The plane came up with a rush, was over on her
back in a flash. For a split second the heads of the

flyers hung toward the earth — and then the ship
was over and coming down with a rush. Then it
happened — with that suddenness and unexpected-
ness with which almost all things happen in the air.

5 There was a sharp crackling; the wing at the left
of the two men suddenly buckled, jerked violently
upward and out of line! At the same time the
ship was leveled off from its downward rush by the
cadet. The engine roared even as Barry screamed

10 a warning — a warning *not* to use power!

The pull of the engine completed the damage.
The left wing cracked again. Both surfaces were
out of line now. A strut collapsed; wires snapped
and sang through the air. The plane lurched badly.

15 The strain of the loop had caused the wing collapse;
the engine pull had finished the job. There was
only one chance now!

Bert Reade jerked his head around as Barry
snapped his safety belt and rose in the rear cockpit.

20 The lieutenant caught the expression of panic in
the cadet's eyes, fought down the fear which was
gripping at him. He moved the joy stick forward
slightly. The throttle he had already jerked back.

"Steady!" he called. "Use your 'chute, Bert!

25 Get clear before you jerk that release ring. It's
all right, Bert!"

He kept his own voice steady with difficulty.
The theory of going over the side with a 'chute was
one thing. He'd had it drilled into him for months.

So had Bert Reade.   But now it was a case of putting the theory into practice.

He saw Bert's hands fumble at his pack, which was strapped on his back.   The ship had begun to go over in a slow spin; he dodged beneath the fuselage level as a taut wire was suddenly snapped and twisted across the fuselage in a violent, screaming whip.

When he looked up again Bert Reade was facing him.   There was stark terror on the cadet's face — and that terror came close to breaking Barry Lewis.   They were down to two thousand feet. It was almost easier to stay in the ship and crash.

He looked down as the stick, which he had released, rattled against his right leg.   And his eyes caught the gleam of the silver wings, the edge of them, showing from within the folds of his light flying coat.   Normally the flying officers did not wear their winged uniforms in the air.   But the colonel's order for Barry to replace the lieutenant who was ill had caught him ready for a trip to town, and he had hurried to the field, stopping only to take his leather flying coat, helmet, and pet goggles.

The gleam of that one silvered wing seemed to give him a sudden courage.   He had fought for that gleam of silver, had worked for it!   It meant something.   It meant that he was supposed to possess the courage for an emergency.   It meant that he had qualified to face just such a situation as this! The colonel had believed that. He was a *flyer* — that was the message, the meaning of those silver wings!

5 His eyes met those of Bert Reade again, but this time they were cold, grim. His voice was low — but steady.

"Get over the side, Bert! I'll follow! Count five — then jerk that release ring! Hurry — we're 10 getting into —"

Less than ten seconds had elapsed since the wing had collapsed utterly. It seemed an eternity to Barry Lewis. He saw Bert jerk himself upright in the fuselage. He saw him reach down, knew that 15 he was snapping the buckle of the safety belt. The Curtiss was starting to spin.

A spasm of fear twisted the cadet's face as he looked into Barry's eyes again. But Barry Lewis had found courage — and that courage shown in 20 the depths of his gray eyes.

"Quick!" he shouted above the screaming of the plane's wires. "We'll make it, Bert! Get loose from the —"

He saw the sudden change in the cadet's expres-25 sion. Bert Reade flung a leg over the side. He seemed to smile. It was something like a smile, at any rate — and then, as the ship twisted into a faster spin, his body seemed to drift clear. He was gone!

14

Barry Lewis closed his eyes for the fraction of a second. His right hand was clutching the nearest strut of the screaming, twisting plane. His left touched the rough, silvered surface of his wings.

Five seconds later he was dropping toward the field. He counted five — jerked the release ring of his lead parachute. He heard the smaller spread of silk snap from the pack, spread. Then, seconds later, he heard the crackling of the great spread of silk the lead parachute had jerked free.

There was a terrific jerking at his shoulders. He sucked in a great breath of the air — and drifted slowly downward. When his eyes were free from tears, caused by the fall, he glanced downward. A few hundred feet below Bert Reade was dropping down beneath the spread silk of his own 'chute. And once more Barry Lewis raised the fingers of his left hand — and touched the silver wings on his left breast.

Colonel Hastings smiled into the keen eyes of Captain Eric Bracket. From their position in the colonel's field office they could see the two lieutenants strolling toward the officers' barracks, side by side.

"When I sent them up together," the colonel said slowly, "I never, of course, thought that the ship would break up. But something told me that the flight would either smash every spark of friendship — or bring back the full fire of it."

Captain Bracket nodded his head. "They showed fine courage," he said simply. "Reade first — and Barry Lewis sticking until Reade got clear."

5   "They'll both make splendid officers," the colonel mused in a low tone. "It takes a man to wear them, and it *makes* a man — to wear them — the silver wings."

LINDBERGH FLIES ALONE

Alone?

Is he alone at whose right side rides Courage,
with Skill within the cockpit and Faith upon the
left? Does solitude surround the brave when
Adventure leads the way and Ambition reads the ₅
dials? Is there no company with him for whom the
air is cleft by Daring and the darkness is made light
by Emprise?

True, the fragile bodies of his fellows do not
weigh down his plane; true, the fretful minds of ₁₀
weaker men are lacking from his crowded cabin;
but as his airship keeps her course, he holds com-
munion with those rarer spirits that inspire to
intrepidity and by their sustaining potency give
strength to arm, resource to mind, content to soul. ₁₅

Alone? With what other companions would
that man fly to whom the choice were given?

Editorial from the *Sun*, May 21, 1927.
Line **14**. **intrepidity:** courage. **potency:** power.

LOST AND FOUND

Octavus Roy Cohen

THE young man was flushed with embarrassment, but his level blue eyes did not waver from the girl's face. He met the issue with courageous honesty and grimly refused to spare himself.

5 "I should have told you at first, Elinor, that I found the bracelet."

The eyes of the girl rested caressingly on the gleaming band of sapphires and diamonds which encircled her dimpled arm. She closed the fingers 10 of her other hand about the jewels as though to protect them, and neither by sign nor word did she help the young man who stood before her — flushed and nervous — his yellow hair tousled, his cheeks crimson.

15 "Of course, you must have suspected that I found it," he continued desperately. "I couldn't very well buy you an eight-hundred-dollar bracelet out of my fifty dollars a week salary. You did suspect, didn't you, dear?"

20 Her voice came back with a metallic ring. "I

didn't think about it at all. I just knew that I loved the bracelet more than anything I ever owned."

"I know. . . . That is why I wanted so much to give it to you. That is why I hoped and prayed that I would never find out who owned it. It was this way —" He started from the beginning again, and pieced together the facts which she had caught in fragments:

"I found that bracelet nearly a month ago. I thought of you right away. I wanted more than anything in the world to give it to you. It was something I could never afford. . . . And I watched the papers every day expecting to see an ad in the Lost and Found section — and hoping I wouldn't.

"No ad appeared. Then I inserted an advertisement every day for a week: 'Valuable bracelet found — owner can have on proper identification.' Nobody answered. It seemed as though a miracle had happened. An eight-hundred-dollar bracelet lost and nobody advertising for it, or even watching the papers for an announcement that it had been found. I had done everything possible. There was no one to claim it: it really seemed as though the thing was mine. That was when I gave it to you.

"I should have told you then that I had found it. I — I rather thought you'd ask, because of course

you knew I couldn't afford to buy a thing like that
. . . even though I love you so much."

He paused a moment.   The girl was staring wide-
eyed : her attitude defensive.

5   "This morning I happened to pick up a Nashville
paper.   In the Lost and Found column there I
found this advertisement. Here. . . ." She made
no effort to take the clipping from him, and he
explained it to her. "It describes that bracelet.
10 It gives the owner's name, dear. There isn't any
mistake.   The lady was visiting here — and lost it.
She didn't know where . . . probably didn't miss
the thing until long after she reached home.   The
ad wasn't even supposed to be seen in this town.
15 But the point is this, sweetheart : I know who that
bracelet belongs to.   It must be returned."

The girl inbreathed audibly. "You can't take
it away from me!" she cried. "It is mine.   You
gave it to me."

20   "You don't understand, dear.   I didn't give it
to you, because it wasn't mine to give.   Oh ! You
can hate me for it if you wish.   I should have
explained . . . but that doesn't alter circumstances.
And I know you wouldn't have me less than honest."

25   "You gave it to me !   It's mine !"

"No, dear. . . ." He spoke patiently, as though
explaining a delicate question of ethics to a child.
"It belongs to the woman in Nashville.   I must
return it to her."

Then she tore away from him and clasped her right hand about
the bracelet.

"But that is silly! Suppose you had never seen her advertisement? She will never know."

"I did see it, though." He rose and crossed to her, attempting to take her in his arms. She did not resist, but her body was rigid and her eyes wide with horrid fear. Then she tore away from him and clasped her right hand about the bracelet.

"You shan't have it!" she cried hysterically. "You gave it to me. I didn't know it wasn't yours. I didn't know you had found it. It isn't fair to give it to me, then come and take it away."

"But, dear — it wouldn't be —"

"I have nothing to do with that. It's mine! You gave it to me! And I won't give it back! I won't!"

Her body was tense, her eyes blazed. The young man stared. The flush was gone from his face, leaving instead a deadly pallor. His eyes were level — and bleak.

"You mean that?"

"I do. I won't give it up. . . ."

"Very well." He spoke now with perfect self-possession. "It is all my fault. I really should have told you — and I didn't. But you can't keep that bracelet. It isn't yours because it wasn't mine to give. But I have decided what we will do. In the morning we will go down to the best jewelry store in the city and I will buy you an exact duplicate of that bracelet. I can arrange to pay

21

for it on weekly terms. They know me there. . . . Then you will have the bracelet, and the lady in Nashville will have hers. . . ."

"You mean that!" she gasped.

5 "Certainly. It is the only proper thing to do." She stepped close and swept her arms about his neck. "Oh! you darling. . . . You great, big darling boy!"

It was two months later, when he stopped in the 10 jewelry store to make his ninth payment on an eight-hundred-dollar bracelet, that the jeweler, a fatherly gentleman who really liked the lad, ventured to question him.

"Didn't you go a bit out of your depth on that 15 bracelet, son," he asked, "even for an engaged man?"

The boy looked up and smiled. "I'm not engaged any more," he answered simply, and just as simply he finished:

20 "It's cheap at the price — fifteen a week for what I found out — and found out in time."

THE RIVERMAN

Stewart Edward White

I FIRST met him one Fourth of July afternoon in
the middle eighties. The sawdust streets and high
board sidewalks of the lumber town were filled to the
brim with people. The permanent population,
dressed in the stiffness of its Sunday best, escorted 5
gingham wives or sweethearts; a dozen outsiders
like me tried not to be too conspicuous in a city
smartness; but the great multitude was composed
of the men of the woods. I sat, chair-tilted, by the
hotel, watching them pass. Their heavy woolen 10
shirts crossed by the broad suspenders, the red of
their sashes or leather shine of their belts, their
short kersey trousers, "stagged" off to leave a gap
between the knee and the heavily spiked "cork
boots" — all these were distinctive enough of their 15
class, but most interesting to me were the eyes
that peered from beneath their little round hats
tilted rakishly askew. They were all subtly alike,
those eyes. Some were black, some were brown, or

Reprinted from Stewart Edward White's *The Riverman* by permission of Brandt and Brandt.
LINE **13.** kersey: a light-weight beaver cloth. **18.** rakishly:
jauntily. askew: in an oblique position.

gray, or blue, but all were steady and unabashed, all looked straight at you with a strange humorous blending of aggression and respect for your own business, and all without exception wrinkled at the 5 corners with a suggestion of dry humor. In my half-conscious scrutiny I probably stared harder than I knew, for, all at once, a laughing pair of the blue eyes suddenly met mine full, and an ironical voice drawled:

10 "Say, bub, you look as interested as a man killing snakes. Am I your long-lost friend?"

The tone of the voice matched accurately the attitude of the man, and that was quite noncommittal. He stood cheerfully ready to meet the 15 emergency. If I sought trouble, it was here to my hand; or if I needed help, he was willing to offer it.

"I guess you are," I replied, "if you can tell me what all this outfit's headed for."

He thrust back his hat and ran his hand through 20 a mop of closely cropped light curls.

"Birling match," he exclaimed briefly. "Come on."

I joined him, and together we followed the crowd to the river, where we roosted like cormorants on 25 adjacent piles overlooking a patch of clear water among the filled booms.

LINE **8.** ironical: with veiled sarcasm. **13.** noncommittal: without expressing opinion. **24.** cormorants: web-footed birds that catch fish. **26.** booms: chains of logs.

The Riverman

"Drive's just over," my new friend informed me. "Rear come down last night. Fourther July celebration. This little town will scratch fer th' tall timber along about midnight when the boys goes in to take her apart." 5

A half-dozen men with peavies rolled a white pine log of about a foot and a half diameter into the clear water, where it lay rocking back and forth, three or four feet from the boom piles. Suddenly a man ran the length of the boom, leaped easily 10 into the air, and landed with both feet square on one end of the floating log. That end disappeared in an ankle-deep swirl of white foam, the other rose suddenly, the whole timber, projected forward by the shock, drove headlong to the middle of the little 15 pond. And the man, his arms folded, his knees just bent in the graceful, nervous attitude of the circus rider, stood upright like a statue of bronze.

A roar approved this feat.

"That's Dickey Darrell," said my informant; 20 "Roaring Dick. Watch him."

The man on the log was small, with clean beautiful haunches and shoulders, but with hanging baboon arms. Perhaps his most striking feature was a mop of reddish-brown hair that overshadowed 25 a little triangular white face accented by two

---

LINE **3.** **scratch fer th' tall timber:** run away. **6. peavies:** hooked levers used in handling logs.

reddish-brown quadrilaterals, serving as eyebrows, and a pair of inscrutable chipmunk eyes.

For a moment he poised erect in the great calm of the public performer. Then slowly he began
5 to revolve the log under his feet. The lofty gaze, the folded arms, the straight supple waist budged not by a hair's breadth; only the feet stepped forward, at first deliberately, then faster and faster, until the rolling log threw a blue spray a foot into
10 the air. Then suddenly slap! slap! the heavy calks stamped a reversal. The log came instantaneously to rest, quivering exactly like some animal that had been spurred through its paces.

"Magnificent!" I cried.
15 "That's nothing!" my companion repressed me; "anybody can birl a log. Watch this."

Roaring Dick for the first time unfolded his arms. With some appearance of caution he balanced his unstable footing into absolute immobility. Then he
20 turned a somersault.

This was the real thing. My friend uttered a wild yell of applause which was lost in a general roar.

A long pike pole shot out, bit the end of the timber, and towed it to the boom pile. Another
25 man stepped on the log with Darrell. They stood facing each other, bent-kneed, alert. Suddenly with one accord they commenced to birl the log

---

LINE **16. birl:** to spin or turn rapidly. **19. unstable:** unsteady. **immobility:** fixedness.

from left to right. The pace grew hot. Like squirrels treading a cage their feet twinkled. Then it became apparent that Darrell's opponent was gradually being forced from the top of the log. He could not keep up. Little by little, still moving 5 desperately, he dropped back to the slant, then at last to the edge, and so off into the river with a mighty splash.

"Clean birled!" commented my friend.

One after another a half-dozen rivermen tackled 10 the imperturbable Dick, but none of them possessed the agility to stay on top in the pace he set them. One boy of eighteen seemed for a moment to hold his own, and managed at least to keep out of the water even when Darrell had apparently reached 15 his maximum speed. But that expert merely threw his entire weight into two reversing stamps of his feet, and the young fellow drove forward as abruptly as though he had been shied over a horse's head.

The crowd was by now getting uproarious and 20 impatient of volunteer effort to humble Darrell's challenge. It wanted the best, and at once. It began, with increasing insistence, to shout a name.

"Jimmy Powers!" it vociferated; "Jimmy Powers." 25

And then by shamefaced bashfulness, by profane protest, by muttered and comprehensive curses,

---

LINE **27**. **comprehensive:** large in content.

The Magic Spear

I knew that my companion on the other pile was indicated.

A dozen men near at hand began to shout. "Here he is!" they cried. "Come on, Jimmy." 5 "Don't be a high banker." "Hang his hide on the fence."

Jimmy, still red and swearing, suffered himself to be pulled from his elevation and disappeared in the throng. A moment later I caught his head and 10 shoulders pushing toward the boom piles, and so in a moment he stepped warily aboard to face his antagonist.

This was evidently no question to be determined by the simplicity of force or the simplicity of a 15 child's trick. The two men stood half-crouched, face to face, watching each other narrowly, but making no move. To me they seemed like two wrestlers sparring for an opening. Slowly the log revolved one way; then slowly the other. It was a 20 mere courtesy of salute. All at once Dick birled three rapid strokes from left to right, as though about to roll the log, leaped into the air and landed square with both feet on the other slant of the timber. Jimmy Powers felt the jar, and acknowledged 25 it by the spasmodic jerk with which he counterbalanced Darrell's weight. But he was not thrown.

As though this daring and hazardous maneuver

LINE **27.** **maneuver:** a dexterous move.

28

The Riverman

had opened the combat, both men sprang to life.
Sometimes the log rolled one way, sometimes the
other; sometimes it jerked from side to side like a
crazy thing, but always with the rapidity of light,
always in a smother of spray and foam. The 5
decided spat, spat, spat of the reversing blows from
the calked boots sounded like picket firing. I
could not make out the different leads, feints, parries, and counters of this strange method of boxing,
nor could I distinguish to whose initiative the vari- 10
ous evolutions of that log could be ascribed. But I
retain still a vivid mental picture of two men nearly
motionless above the waist, nearly vibrant below
it, dominating the insane gyrations of a stick of
pine. 15

The crowd was appreciative and partisan — for
Jimmy Powers. It howled wildly, and rose thereby
to ever higher excitement. Then it forgot its
manners utterly and groaned when it made out
that a sudden splash represented its favorite, while 20
the indomitable Darrell still trod the quarter-deck
as champion birler for the year.

I must confess I was as sorry as anybody. I
climbed down from my cormorant roost, and picked
my way between the alleys of aromatic piled lumber 25

LINE **8. leads, feints, parries, and counters:** terms used in
boxing. **10. initiative:** first move. **14. gyrations:** turn-
ings. **21. indomitable:** untamable. **25. aromatic:** having
a spicy odor.

in order to avoid the press, and cursed the little gods
heartily for undue partiality in the wrong direction.
In this manner I happened on Jimmy Powers
himself seated dripping on a board and examining
5 his bared foot.

"I'm sorry," said I behind him. "How did he
do it?"

He whirled, and I could see that his laughing
boyish face had become suddenly grim and stern,
10 and that his eyes were shot with blood.

"Oh, it's you, is it?" he growled disparagingly.
"Well, that's how he did it."

He held out his foot. Across the instep and at
the base of the toes ran two rows of tiny round
15 punctures from which the blood was oozing. I
looked very inquiring.

"He corked me!" Jimmy Powers explained.
"Jammed his spikes into me! Stepped on my foot
and tripped me, the ——." Jimmy Powers
20 certainly could swear.

"Why didn't you make a kick?" I cried.

"That ain't how I do it," he muttered, pulling
on his heavy woolen sock.

"But no," I insisted, my indignation mounting.
25 "It's an outrage! That crowd was with you. All
you had to do was to say something —"

He cut me short. "And give myself away as a

---

fool — sure Mike. I ought to know Dickey Darrell by this time, and I ought to be big enough to take care of myself." He stamped his foot into his driver's shoe and took me by the arm, his good humor apparently restored. "No, don't you lose any hair, bub; I'll get even with Roaring Dick."

That night, having by the advice of the proprietor moved my bureau and trunk against the bedroom door, I lay wide awake listening to the taking of the town apart. At each especially vicious crash I wondered if that might be Jimmy Powers getting even with Roaring Dick.

The following year, but earlier in the season, I again visited my little lumber town. In striking contrast to the life of that other midsummer day were the deserted streets. The landlord knew me, and after I had washed and eaten, approached me with a suggestion.

"You got all day in front of you," said he. "Why don't you take a horse and buggy and make a visit to the big jam? Everybody's up there more or less."

In response to my inquiry he replied:

"They've jammed at the upper bend, jammed bad. The crew's been picking at her for near a week now, and last night Darrell was down to see about some more dynamite. It's worth seein'. The breast of her is near thirty foot high, and lots of water in the river."

"Darrell?" said I, catching at the name.

"Yes. He's rear boss this year. Do you think you'd like to take a look at her?"

"I think I should," I assented.

5 The horse and I jogged slowly along a deep sand road, through wastes of pine stumps and belts of

In another moment I looked down on the jam.

hardwood beautiful with the early spring, until finally we arrived at a clearing in which stood two huge tents, a mammoth kettle slung over a fire of 10 logs, and drying racks about the timbers of another fire. A fat cook in the inevitable battered derby hat, two bare-armed cookees, and a chore "boy" of seventy-odd summers were the only human beings in sight. One of the cookees agreed to keep 15 an eye on my horse. I picked my way down a well-

32

worn trail toward the regular clank, clank, click of the peavies.

I emerged finally to a plateau elevated some fifty or sixty feet above the river. A half-dozen spectators were already gathered. Among them I could not but notice a tall, spare, broad-shouldered young fellow dressed in a quiet business suit, somewhat wrinkled, whose square, strong, clean-cut face and muscular hands were tanned by the weather to a dark umber-brown. In another moment I looked down on the jam.

The breast, as my landlord had told me, rose sheer from the water to the height of at least twenty-five feet, bristling and formidable. Back of it pressed the volume of logs packed closely in an apparently inextricable tangle as far as the eye could reach. A man near informed me that the tail was a good three miles up stream. From beneath this wonderful *cheval de frise* foamed the current of the river, irresistible to any force less mighty than the statics of such a mass.

A crew of forty or fifty men were at work. They clamped their peavies to the reluctant timbers, heaved, pushed, slid, and rolled them one by one into the current, where they were caught and borne away. They had been doing this for a week. As yet their efforts had made but slight impression

---

LINE **19.** *cheval de frise:* an obstacle of projecting spikes.
21. statics: equilibrium; inertia.

on the bulk of the jam, but some time, with patience,
they would reach the key logs. Then the tangle
would melt like sugar in the freshet, and these
imperturbable workers would have to escape suddenly over the plunging logs to shore.

My eye ranged over the men, and finally rested
on Dickey Darrell. He was standing on the slanting end of an upheaved log dominating the scene.
His little triangular face with the accents of the
quadrilateral eyebrows was pale with the blaze of
his energy, and his chipmunk eyes seemed to flame
with a dynamic vehemence that caused those on
whom their glance fell to jump as though they had
been touched with a hot poker. I had heard more
of Dickey Darrell since my last visit, and was glad
of the chance to observe Morrison and Daly's best
"driver" at work.

The jam seemed on the very edge of breaking.
After half an hour's strained expectation, it seemed
still on the very edge of breaking. So I sat down on
a stump. Then for the first time I noticed another
acquaintance, handling his peavey near the very
person of the rear boss.

"Hullo," said I to myself; "that's funny. I
wonder if Jimmy Powers got even; and if so, why
he is working so amicably and so near Roaring
Dick."

LINE **12.** **dynamic:** efficient; forceful. **vehemence:** intensity.

At noon the men came ashore for dinner. I paid a quarter into the cook's private exchequer and so was fed. After the meal I approached my acquaintance of the year before.

"Hello, Powers," I greeted him; "I suppose 5 you don't remember me?"

"Sure," he responded heartily. "Ain't you a little early this year?"

"No," I disclaimed, "this is a better sight than a birling match." 10

I offered him a cigar, which he immediately substituted for his corncob pipe. We sat at the root of a tree.

"It'll be a great sight when that jam pulls," said I.

"You bet," he replied, "but she's a teaser. Even 15 old Tim Shearer would have a picnic to make out just where the key logs are. We've started her three times, but she's plugged tight every trip. Likely to pull almost any time."

We discussed various topics. Finally I ven- 20 tured:

"I see your old friend Darrell is rear boss."

"Yes," said Jimmy Powers dryly.

"By the way, did you fellows ever square up on that birling match?" 25

"No," said Jimmy Powers; then after an instant, "not yet."

LINE **2.** **exchequer:** purse.

The Magic Spear

I glanced at him to recognize the square set to
the jaw that had impressed me so formidably the
year before. And again his face relaxed almost
quizzically as he caught sight of mine.

5 "Bub," said he, getting to his feet, "those little
marks are on my foot yet. And just you tie into
one idea: Dickey Darrell's got it coming." His
face darkened with a swift anger. I glimpsed the
flare of an undying hate.

10 About three o'clock that afternoon Jimmy's
prediction was fulfilled. Without the slightest
warning the jam "pulled." Usually certain premonitory cracks, certain sinkings down, groanings
forward, grumblings, shruggings, and sullen, reluc-
15 tant shiftings of the logs gave opportunity for the
men to assure their safety. This jam, after inexplicably hanging fire for a week, as inexplicably
started like a sprinter almost into its full gait.
The first few tiers toppled smash into the current,
20 raising a waterspout like that made by a dynamite
explosion; the mass behind plunged forward blindly
rising and falling as the integral logs were up-ended,
turned over, thrust one side, or forced bodily into
the air by the mighty power playing jackstraws
25 with them.

The rivermen, though caught unaware, reached

LINE **4. quizzically:** oddly. **12. premonitory:** warning.
16. inexplicably: unaccountably. **22. integral:** forming a
completed whole.

either bank. They held their peavies across their
bodies as balancing poles, and zigzagged ashore
with a calmness and lack of haste that were in
reality only an indication of the keenness with
which they fore-estimated each chance. Long 5
experience with the ways of saw logs brought them
out. They knew the correlation of these many
forces just as the expert billiard player knows
instinctively the various angles of incidence and
reflection between his cue ball and its mark. Con- 10
sequently, they avoided the centers of eruption,
paused on the spots steadied for the moment, dodged
moving logs, trod those not yet under way, and so
arrived on solid ground. The jam itself started
with every indication of meaning business, gained 15
momentum for a hundred feet, and then plugged to
a standstill. The "break" was abortive.

Now we all had leisure to notice two things.
First, the movement had not been of the whole jam,
as we had at first supposed, but only of a block or 20
section of it twenty rods or so in extent. Thus
between the part that had moved and the greater
bulk that had not stirred lay a hundred feet of open
water in which floated a number of loose logs. The
second fact was that Dickey Darrell had fallen into 25
that open stretch of water and was in the act of
swimming toward one of the floating logs. That

LINE **7. correlation:** relation. **9. incidence:** the striking
of a surface by a body. **17. abortive:** unsuccessful.

much we were given just time to appreciate thoroughly. Then the other section of the jam rumbled and began to break. Roaring Dick was caught between two gigantic millstones moving to crush
5 him out of sight.

An active figure darted down the tail of the first section, out over the floating logs, seized Darrell by the coat collar, and so burdened began desperately to scale the very face of the breaking jam.

10 Never was a more magnificent rescue. The logs were rolling, falling, diving against the laden man. He climbed as over a treadmill, a treadmill whose speed was constantly increasing. And when he finally gained the top, it was as the gap closed
15 splintering beneath him and the man he had saved.

It is not in the woodsman to be demonstrative at any time, but here was work demanding attention. Without a pause for breath or congratulation they turned to the necessity of the moment. The jam,
20 the whole jam, was moving at last. Jimmy Powers ran ashore for his peavey. Roaring Dick, like a demon incarnate, threw himself into the work. Forty men attacked the jam at a dozen places, encouraging the movement, twisting aside the tim-
25 bers that threatened to lock anew, directing pigmy-like the Titanic forces into the channel of their efficiency. Roaring like wild cattle the logs swept

---

LINE **22.** **incarnate:** in living form.

The Riverman

by, at first slowly, then with the railroad rush of
the curbed freshet. Men were everywhere, taking
chances, like cowboys before the stampeded herd.
And so, out of sight around the lower bend swept
the front of the jam in a swirl of glory, the river- 5
men riding the great boom back of the creature they
subdued, until at last, with the slackening current,
the logs floated by free, cannoning with hollow sound
one against another. A half-dozen watchers, leaning statuesquely on the shafts of their peavies, 10
watched the ordered ranks pass by.

One by one the spectators departed. At last
only myself and the brown-faced young man remained. He sat on a stump, staring with sightless
eyes into vacancy. I did not disturb his thoughts. 15

The sun dipped. A cool breeze of evening sucked
up the river. Over near the cook camp a big fire
commenced to crackle by the drying frames. At
dusk the rivermen straggled in from the down-river
trail.
                                                        20

The brown-faced young man arose and went to
meet them. I saw him return in close conversation
with Jimmy Powers. Before they reached us he
had turned away with a gesture of farewell.

Jimmy Powers stood looking after him long after 25
his form had disappeared, and indeed even after
the sound of his wheels had died toward town. As
I approached, the riverman turned to me a face
from which the reckless, contained self-reliance of

the woods-worker had faded. It was wide-eyed
with an almost awe-stricken wonder and adoration.

"Do you know who that is?" he asked me in a
hushed voice. "That's Thorpe, Harry Thorpe.
5 And do you know what he said to me just now, me?
He told me he wanted me to work in Camp One
next winter, Thorpe's One. And he told me I was
the first man he ever hired straight into One."

His breath caught with something like a sob.

10 I had heard of the man and of his methods. I
knew he had made it a practice of recruiting for his
prize camp only from the employees of his other
camps, that, as Jimmy said, he never "hired
straight into One." I had heard, too, of his repu-
15 tation among his own and other woodsmen. But
this was the first time I had ever come into personal
contact with his influence. It impressed me the
more in that I had come to know Jimmy Powers
and his kind.

20 "You deserve it, every bit," said I. "I'm not
going to call you a hero, because that would make
you tired. What you did this afternoon showed
nerve. It was a brave act. But it was a better
act because you rescued your enemy, because you
25 forgot everything but your common humanity when
danger —"

I broke off. Jimmy was again looking at me with
his ironically quizzical grin.

"Bub," said he, "if you're going to hang any

40

stars of Bethlehem on my Christmas tree, just call a halt right here. I didn't rescue that scalawag because I had any Christian sentiments, nary bit. I was just naturally savin' him for the birling match next Fourther July." 5

FISHING ON THE WRONG SIDE

Thomas Nelson Page

WHETHER it was that the best fishing holes were
on Dr. Browne's side of the river, and that the
river duck especially loved the "collard"-filled
cove with its succulent grasses which the back-
5 water from the major's mill pond made on that
bank, or whether it was Bruce's natural and inevitable propensity to do that which was forbidden,
the boy very shortly disobeyed his father's injunc-
tion.   He came home one day with a fine string of
10 fish which he boldly announced that he and Dick
had caught on Dr. Browne's bank.

The major was immediately in a passion. He
declared that Bruce had ruined Dick and made him
a runaway, and wound up by demanding that the
15 boy should with his own hands immediately take
the fish straight back to their owner.

Bruce refused.

There was a pitched battle, in which the major
gave Bruce, as usual, a tremendous thrashing; but
20 received still the same dogged reply he had made

Reprinted from Thomas Nelson Page's *On Newfound River*, copyrighted by Charles Scribner's Sons.
LINE **4.** **succulent:** juicy. **7.** **propensity:** tendency.

42

him from the first, "I won't do it if you kill me."
Then he ordered him to bed.

The boy went, though it was early in the afternoon.

Then his mother, who always acted the peace-maker between the two, went upstairs to him.

Bruce was lying in bed, looking longingly out of
the window. His eyes had an angry gleam in
them, and his mouth was drawn. It is not far,
however, from a mother's heart to her son's, and
in a few moments the boy was weeping in his
mother's arms. Her tenderness brought the sub-
mission which the major's discipline had failed to
secure. Sitting on the bed by the boy, holding his
hand in both of hers, she told him a story.

It was that long years before, when his father was
a boy just his age, he had had an elder brother
named Bruce. He was willful and disobedient;
defied all authority. One day his father, angered
by his insubordination, in a passion said to him that
he was a disgrace to the name he bore. "Then I
will never disgrace it any more," he said angrily;
"for I never will bear it again," and with that he had
rushed out of the house and disappeared. The next
day his hat was found floating on the pond. The
dam was cut, the river was dragged, and every
effort was made to recover the body, but in vain.
It killed his mother, and embittered his father's
whole after life. He never got over it.

Mrs. Landon broke down, weeping at the thought of the sad, bereft mother. She leaned over and drew her son to her bosom, and kissed him again and again.

5 "O Bruce, Bruce! my son! my son!" she sobbed.

In a little while Bruce came down and said he would take the fish back. He, however, announced boldly that he was going because his mother wished him to go, and thought that he ought not to catch 10 fish on another's land without permission, and not because he had been whipped.

The boy's feelings as, after he crossed the river, he rode his colt along the old road through the pines were so strange and so complex that he remembered 15 them years afterwards. It was the first time he had ever been on the place, and he had never seen any one who had been there except Dick Runaway.

The shame he felt as he rode along at having to confess that he had caught the fish on another's 20 property without permission gave way to a feeling of curiosity as he came in sight of the dense hedge of cedars which surrounded the yard as with a wall. The pines grew up almost to the hedge. He passed between two old leaning gateposts from one of 25 which hung the broken fragment of an ancient gate. and found himself in a yard all grown up in weeds and bushes, except on one side where there was a flower garden. Just before him was a long, low, weather-stained frame dwelling with a hipped roof,

44

queer wings, and quaint dormer windows jutting out.

Bruce rode up, and stopped in front of the door. As no one appeared, he called:

"Hello!"

From an old and ruinous outbuilding came back "Hello!" but there was no one in sight.

"Hello!" he called again, and again came the short reply, "Hello!" which he found was nothing but an echo from the old building at the side.

After waiting a moment, he decided that he could not have been seen, and rode on and tied his horse to an overhanging limb, and went up to the door.

He knocked. The stillness was so intense that the sound of his rapping made him jump. The odors of the locust blossoms became oppressive and the hum of the bees among them filled all the silence. He was about to leave and go around to the other side of the house, when a door opened at the far end of the passage, and an elderly negro woman, thin and black, and with her head tied up in a blue checked handkerchief, appeared and came slowly toward him.

"Good evening," said Bruce, and then, without waiting for her to speak, began rapidly:

"Here is a string of fish I caught down yonder on your side of the pond, and my mother sent me to bring them back." He paused to swallow, for his throat was dry.

"Who you say sent 'em?" asked the woman, looking at them curiously.

"My mother — my father — Major Landon. I caught them."

5 The woman's face brightened.

"Thankee, little marster," she said.

The boy saw that she considered them a present. The temptation was strong to leave her under the impression; for he had told her once why he had 10 brought them back; but Bruce was as honest as day. A Landon would not lie. He thought of that saying of Brian de Bois Guilbert, "Many a law and many a commandment have I broken; but my word never," and he gulped out:

15 "They are not a present — I caught them on this side — on your side, and my mother — and my father — sent them back: my father is Major Landon."

"What's all this?" inquired a stern voice.

20 Bruce turned in amazement at the sound of the voice. An old gentleman, tall and gray, stood behind him.

"What was that you were saying?" he asked sharply, his keen dark eyes gleaming from beneath 25 his shaggy white eyebrows. The stern voice and the flash of the deep eyes above the eaglelike nose seemed so familiar to the boy that he insensibly assumed a hostile attitude. But he went through his formula honestly.

46

The sturdy honesty of the boy and the evident struggle he
underwent attracted the old man.

Fishing on the Wrong Side

"I caught some fish on your side of the river, and I have brought them back, as my mother and father thought I ought not to have done it without permission."

The sturdy honesty of the boy and the evident struggle he underwent attracted the old man, and a kindly light stole into his eyes.

"So you caught them without permission, did you, and they made you bring them back?"

A curious look shone even through his long beard.

"I brought them because my mother wanted me to do it," said Bruce doggedly.

"Oh, because your mother wanted it?" he muttered. He had averted his face slightly, but now he turned to the boy, and laying his hand on his head, he said gently:

"You have my permission to fish or hunt, or do anything you wish anywhere on my property; but, my son, remember this, 'Honor thy father and thy mother, that thy days may be long in the land which the Lord thy God giveth thee.'" He suddenly turned and walked into the house.

When Bruce came home that night he avowed himself the friend of his new acquaintance, and from that time he was his steadfast champion.

FISHING

Selma Lagerlöf

I⊤ would hardly have been possible for any one
to be as fond of the little girl as her father was; but
it may be truly said that she had a very good friend
in old seine-maker Ola.

5   This is the way they came to be friends: Glory
Goldie had taken to setting out fishing poles in the
brook for the small salmon trout that abounded
there.   She had better luck with her fishing than
any one would have expected, and the very first day
10 she brought home two spindly fishes.

She was elated over her success, as can be
imagined, and received praise from her mother for
being able to provide food for the family, when she
was only a little girl of eight.   To encourage the
15 child, Katrina let her cleanse and fry the fish.   Jan
ate of it and declared he had never tasted the like
of that fish, which was the plain truth.   For the
fish was so bony and dry and burnt that the little
girl herself could scarcely swallow a morsel of it.

Reprinted from Selma Lagerlöf's *The Emperor of Portugallia* by permission of Doubleday, Page & Co.
    LINE 4.   seine-maker: net-maker.

Fishing

But for all that the little girl was just as enthusiastic over her fishing. She got up every morning at the same time that Jan did and hurried off to the brook, a basket on her arm, carrying in a little tin box the worms to bait her hooks. Thus 5 equipped, she went off to the brook, which came gushing down the rocky steep in numerous falls and rapids, between which were short stretches of dark still water and places where the stream ran, clear and transparent, over a bed of sand and 10 smooth stones.

Think of it! After the first week she had no luck with the fishing. The worms were gone from all the hooks, but no fish had fastened there. She shifted her tackle from rapid to still water, from still water 15 to rippling falls, and she changed her hooks — but with no better results.

She asked the boys at Börje's and at Eric's if they were not the ones who got up with the lark and carried off her fish. But a question like that the 20 boys would not deign to answer. For no boy would stoop to take fish from the brook, when he had the whole Dove Lake to fish in. It was all right for little girls, who were not allowed to go down to the lake, to run about hunting fish in the woods, they 25 said.

Despite the superior airs of the boys, the little girl only half believed them. "Surely some one must take the fish off my hooks!" she said to herself. Hers were real hooks, too, and not just bent pins. And in order to satisfy herself she arose one morning before Jan and Katrina were awake, and ran over to the brook. When near to the stream she slackened her pace, taking very short cautious steps so as not to slip on the stones or to rustle the bushes. Then, all at once, her whole body became numb. For at the edge of the brook, on the very spot where she had set out her poles the morning before, stood a fish thief tampering with her lines. It was not one of the boys, as she had supposed, but a grown man, who was just then bending over the water, drawing up a fish.

Little Glory Goldie was never afraid. She rushed right up to the thief and caught him in the act.

"So you're the one who comes here and takes my fish!" she said. "It's a good thing I've run across you at last so we can put a stop to this stealing."

The man then raised his head, and now Glory Goldie saw his face. It was the old seine-maker, who was one of their neighbors.

"Yes, I know this is your tackle," the man admitted, without getting angry or excited, as most folks do when taken to task for wrongdoing.

"But how can you take what isn't yours?" asked the puzzled youngster.

The man looked straight at her; she never forgot that look; she seemed to be peering into two open

For at the edge of the brook stood a fish thief tampering with
her lines.

and empty caverns at the back of which were a pair of half-dead eyes, beyond reflecting either joy or grief.

"Well, you see, I'm aware that you get what you require from your parents and that you fish only for the fun of it, while at my home we are starving."

The little girl flushed. Now she felt ashamed.

The seine-maker said nothing further, but picked up his cap (it had dropped from his head while he was bending over the fishing poles) and went his way. Nor did Glory Goldie speak. Two fishes lay floundering on the ground, but she did not take them up; when she had stood a while looking at them, she kicked them back into the water.

All that day the little girl felt displeased with herself, without knowing why. For indeed it was not she who had done wrong. She could not get the seine-maker out of her thoughts. The old man was said to have been rich at one time; he had once owned seven big farmsteads, each in itself worth as much as Eric of Falla's farm. But in some unaccountable way he had disposed of his property and was now quite penniless.

However, the next morning Glory Goldie went over to the brook the same as usual. This time no one had touched her hooks, for now there was a fish at the end of every line. She released the fishes

51

from the hooks and laid them in her basket; but instead of going home with her catch she went straight to the seine-maker's cabin.

When the little girl came along with her basket, the old man was out in the yard, cutting wood. She stood at the stile a moment, watching him, before stepping over. He looked pitifully poor and ragged. Even her father had never appeared so shabby.

The little girl had heard that some well-to-do people had offered the seine-maker a home for life, but in preference he had gone to live with his daughter-in-law, who made her home here in the Ashdales, so as to help her in any way that he could; she had many children, and her husband, who had deserted her, was now supposed to be dead.

"To-day there were fish on the hooks!" shouted the little girl from the stile.

"You don't tell me!" said the seine-maker. "But that was well."

"I'll gladly give you all the fish I catch," she told him, "if I'm only allowed to do the fishing myself." So saying, she went up to the seine-maker and emptied the contents of her basket on the ground, expecting of course that he would be pleased and would praise her, just as her father — who was always pleased with everything she said or did — had always done. But the seine-maker took this attention with his usual calm indifference.

"You keep what's yours," he said. "We're so

used to going hungry here that we can get on without your few little fishes."

There was something out of the common about
this poor old man and Glory Goldie was anxious
to win his approval.   5

"You may take the fish off and stick the worms
on the hooks, if you like," said she, "and you can
have all the tackle and everything."

"Thanks," returned the old man. "But I'll
not deprive you of your pleasure."   10

Glory Goldie was determined not to go until she
had thought out a way of satisfying him.

"Would you like me to come and call for you
every morning," she asked him, "so that we could
draw up the lines together and divide the catch — 15
you get half, and I half?"

Then the old man stopped chopping and rested
on the ax. He turned his strange, half-dead eyes
toward the child, and the shadow of a smile crossed
his face.   20

"Ah, now you put out the right bait!" he said.
"That proposition I'll not say no to."

THE FINGER OF GOD

Percival Wilde

STRICKLAND. Close the window, Benson: it's cold.

BENSON (*goes to the window*). The window is closed, sir. It's been closed all evening.

5 STRICKLAND (*shivers and buttons his coat tightly*). Benson.

BENSON. Yes, sir?

STRICKLAND. Don't forget a heavy overcoat.

BENSON. I've put it in already, sir.

10 STRICKLAND. Plenty of fresh linen?

BENSON. Yes, sir.

STRICKLAND. Collars and ties?

BENSON. I've looked out for everything, sir.

STRICKLAND (*after a pause*). You sent off the
15 trunks this afternoon?

BENSON. Yes, sir.

STRICKLAND. You're sure they can't be traced?

BENSON. I had one wagon take them to a vacant lot, and another wagon take them to the station.   5

STRICKLAND. Good!

BENSON. I checked them through to Chicago. Here are the checks. (*He hands them over.*) What train do we take, sir?

STRICKLAND. I take the midnight. You follow 10 me sometime next week. We mustn't be seen leaving town together.

BENSON. How will I find you in Chicago?

STRICKLAND. You won't. You'll take rooms somewhere, and I'll take rooms somewhere else till 15 it's all blown over. When I want you, I'll put an ad in the *Tribune*.

BENSON. You don't know when that will be, sir?

STRICKLAND. As soon as I think it is safe. It 20 may be two weeks. It may be a couple of months. But you will stay in Chicago till you hear from me one way or the other. You understand?

BENSON. Yes, sir.

STRICKLAND. Have you plenty of money?   25

BENSON. Not enough to last a couple of months.

STRICKLAND (*producing a large pocketbook*). How much do you want?

BENSON. Five or six hundred.

The Magic Spear

STRICKLAND (*takes out a few bills; stops*). Wait a minute! I left that much in my bureau drawer. (*He goes toward the door.*)

BENSON. Mr. Strickland?

5 STRICKLAND. Yes?

BENSON. It's the midnight train for Chicago, isn't it?

STRICKLAND. Yes. (*He goes into the next room.*)

BENSON (*waits an instant, then lifts the telephone*
10 *receiver and speaks very quietly*). Hello. Murray Hill 3500. . . . Hello. This Finley? This is Benson. . . . He's going to take the midnight train for Chicago. Pennsylvania. You had better arrest him at the station. If he once gets to Chi-
15 cago you'll never find him. And, Finley, you won't forget me, will you? . . . I want five thousand dollars for it. Yes, five thousand. That's little enough. He's got almost three hundred thousand on him, and you won't turn in all of that to Head-
20 quarters. Yes, it's cash. Large bills. (*Strickland's step is heard.*) Midnight for Chicago.

(*Benson hangs up the receiver and is busy with the suitcase as Strickland enters.*)

STRICKLAND. Here's your money, Benson.
25 Count it.

BENSON (*after counting*). Six hundred dollars; thank you, sir. (*He picks up the closed suitcase.*) Shall I go now?

STRICKLAND. No. Wait a minute. (*He goes*

The Finger of God

to the telephone.) Hello. Madison Square 7900.
. . . Pennsylvania? I want a stateroom for
Chicago, midnight train. Yes, to-night.

BENSON. Don't give your own name, sir.

STRICKLAND. No. The name is Stevens. . . ₅
Oh, you have one reserved in that name already?
Well, this is Alfred Stevens. . . . You have it
reserved in that name? Then give me another
stateroom. . . . What? You haven't any other.
(*He pauses in an instant's thought; then, decisively*) ₁₀
Never mind, then. Good-by. (*He turns to
Benson.*) Benson, go right down to the Pennsylvania, and get the stateroom that is reserved
for Alfred Stevens. You've got to get there before
he does. Wait for me at the train gate. ₁₅

BENSON. Yes, sir.

STRICKLAND. Don't waste any time. I'll see
you later.

BENSON. Very well, sir. (*He takes up the suitcase and goes.*) ₂₀

(*Left alone Strickland opens drawer after drawer of
the desk systematically, dumping what few papers are
still left into the fire. Outside, a wintry gale whistles,
and shakes the locked window. Suddenly there is a
knock at the door. He pauses, very much startled.* ₂₅
*A little wait, and then the knock, a single knock, is
repeated. He rises, goes to the door, opens it. A
girl enters. She is young: certainly under thirty;
perhaps under twenty-five; possibly still younger.*

The Magic Spear

A somewhat shabby boa of some dark fur encircles her
neck, and makes her pallid face stand out with startling
distinctness from beneath a mass of lustrous brown
hair. As she steps over the threshold she gives a little
5 *shiver of comfort, for it is cold outside, and her thin*
shoulders have been shielded from the driving snow by
a threadbare coat. She enters the warm room grate-
fully, and little rivulets of melted ice trickle to the
floor from her inadequate clothing. Her lips are blue.
10 *Her hands tremble in their worn white gloves. A seat*
before a blazing fire, or perhaps a sip of some strong
cordial — this is what she needs. But Strickland
has no time for such things. He greets her with a
volley of questions.)

15 STRICKLAND. Who are you?

THE GIRL. Why, don't you remember me, sir?

STRICKLAND. No.

THE GIRL. I'm from the office, sir.

STRICKLAND. The office?

20 THE GIRL. Your office. I'm one of your personal stenographers, sir.

STRICKLAND. Oh. I suppose I didn't recognize
you on account of the hat. What do you want?

THE GIRL. There were some letters which came
25 late this afternoon —

STRICKLAND (*interrupting harshly*). And you're
bothering me with them now? (*He crosses to the
door, and holds it open.*) I've got no time. Good
night.

58

The Finger of God

THE GIRL (*timidly*). I thought you'd want to see these letters.

STRICKLAND. Plenty of time to-morrow.

THE GIRL. But you won't be here to-morrow, will you? 5

STRICKLAND (*starting violently*). Won't be here? What do you mean?

THE GIRL. You're taking the train to Chicago to-night.

STRICKLAND. How did you know — (*He stops* 10 *himself; then, with forced ease*) Taking a train to Chicago? Of course not! What put that in your head?

THE GIRL. Why, you told me, sir.

STRICKLAND. I told you? 15

THE GIRL. You said so this afternoon.

STRICKLAND (*harshly*). I didn't see you this afternoon.

THE GIRL (*without contradicting him*). No, sir? (*She produces a time-table.*) Then I found this 20 time-table. (*She holds it out. He snatches it.*)

STRICKLAND. Where did you find it?

THE GIRL. On your desk, sir.

STRICKLAND. On my desk?

THE GIRL. Yes, sir. 25

STRICKLAND (*suddenly and directly*). You're lying.

THE GIRL. Why, Mr. Strickland!

STRICKLAND. That time-table never reached my

59

desk! I lost it between the railroad station and my office.

THE GIRL. Did you, sir? But it's the same time-table; you see, you checked the midnight
5 train. (*He looks at her suspiciously.*) I reserved a stateroom for you.

STRICKLAND (*astonished*). You reserved a stateroom?

THE GIRL (*smiling*). I knew you'd forget it.
10 You have your head so full of other things. So I telephoned as soon as you left the office.

STRICKLAND (*biting his lip angrily*). I suppose you made the reservation in my own name?

THE GIRL. No, sir.

15 STRICKLAND (*immensely surprised*). What?

THE GIRL. I thought you'd prefer some other name: you didn't want your trip to be known.

STRICKLAND. No, I didn't. (*A good deal startled, he looks at her as if he were about to ask,*
20 "*How did you know that?*" *She returns his gaze unflinchingly. The question remains unasked. But a sudden thought strikes him.*) What name did you give?

THE GIRL. Stevens, sir.

25 STRICKLAND (*thunderstruck*). Stevens?

THE GIRL. Alfred Stevens.

STRICKLAND (*gasping*). What made you choose that name?

THE GIRL. I don't know, sir.

STRICKLAND. You don't know?

THE GIRL. No, sir. It was just the first name that popped into my head. I said "Stevens," and when the clerk asked for the first name, I said "Alfred."

STRICKLAND (*after a pause*). Have you ever known anybody of that name?

THE GIRL. No, sir.

STRICKLAND (*with curious insistence*). You are sure you never knew anybody of that name?

THE GIRL. How can I be sure? I may have; I don't remember it.

STRICKLAND (*abruptly*). How old are you? (*He gives her no time to answer.*) You're not twenty, are you?

THE GIRL (*smiling*). Do you think so?

STRICKLAND (*continuing the current of his thoughts*). And I'm forty-seven. It was more than twenty-five years ago. . . . You couldn't have known.

THE GIRL (*after a pause*). No, sir.

STRICKLAND (*looking at her with something of fear in his eye*). What is your name?

THE GIRL. Does it matter? You didn't recognize my face a few minutes ago : my name can't mean much to you. I'm just one of the office force ; I'm the girl who answers when you push the button three times. (*She opens a hand bag.*) These are the letters I brought with me.

The Magic Spear

STRICKLAND (*not offering to take them*). What are they about?

THE GIRL (*opening the first*). This is from a woman who wants to invest some money.

5 STRICKLAND. How much?

THE GIRL. Only a thousand dollars.

STRICKLAND. Why didn't you turn it over to the clerks?

THE GIRL. The savings of a lifetime, she writes.

10 STRICKLAND. What of it?

THE GIRL. She wrote that she had confidence in you. She says that she wants you to invest it for her yourself.

STRICKLAND. You shouldn't have bothered me
15 with that. Every man who has five dollars to invest asks the head of the firm to attend to it himself. It means nothing. I get hundreds of letters like those.

THE GIRL. Still —

20 STRICKLAND. What?

THE GIRL. You must do something to deserve such letters or they wouldn't keep on coming in. (*She smiles.*) It's a wonderful thing to inspire such confidence in people.

25 STRICKLAND. Do you think so?

THE GIRL. It is more than wonderful! It is magnificent! These people don't know you from Adam. Not one in a hundred has seen you; not one in a thousand calls you by your first name.

But they've all heard of you; you're as real to them as if you were a member of their family. And what is even more real than you is your reputation! Something in which they rest their absolute confidence; something in which they place their implicit trust!

STRICKLAND (*slowly*). So you think there are few honest men?

THE GIRL. No: there are many of them. But there is something about you that is different: something in the tone of your voice, something in the way you shake hands, something in the look of your eye, that is reassuring. There is never a doubt — never a question about you. Oh, it's splendid! Simply splendid! (*She pauses.*) What a satisfaction it must be to you to walk along the street and know that every one you meet must say to himself, "There goes an honest man!" It's been such an inspiration to me!

STRICKLAND. To you?

THE GIRL. Oh, I know that I'm just one of the office force to you. You don't even know my name. But you don't imagine that any one can see you as I have seen you, can work with you as I have worked with you, without there being some kind of an effect? You know, in my own troubles —

STRICKLAND (*interrupting*). So you have troubles?

THE GIRL. You don't pay me a very big salary,

and there are others whom I must help. But I'm not complaining. (*She smiles*.) I — I used to be like the other girls. I used to watch the clock. I used to count the hours and the minutes till the day's work was over. But it's different now.

STRICKLAND (*slowly*). How — different?

THE GIRL. I thought it over, and I made up my mind that it wasn't right to count the minutes you worked for an honest man. (*Strickland turns away*.) And there is a new pleasure in my work. I do my best — that's all I can do — but you do your best; and it's the least I can do.

STRICKLAND (*after a pause*). Are you sure — I do my best? Are you sure I am an honest man?

THE GIRL. Don't you know it yourself, Mr. Strickland?

STRICKLAND (*after another pause*). You remember — a few minutes ago, you spoke the name of Alfred Stevens?

THE GIRL. Yes.

STRICKLAND. Suppose I told you that there once was an Alfred Stevens? (*The girl does not answer*.) Suppose I told you that Stevens, whom I knew, stole money — stole it when there was no excuse for it — when he didn't need it. His people had plenty, and they gave him plenty. But the chance came, and he couldn't resist the temptation. He was eighteen years old then.

THE GIRL (*gently*). Only a boy.

The Finger of God

STRICKLAND. Only a boy, yes, but he had the dishonest streak in him! Other boys passed by the same opportunity. Stevens didn't even know what to do with the money when he had stolen it. They caught him in less than twenty-four hours. ₅ It was almost funny.

THE GIRL. He was punished.

STRICKLAND (*nodding*). He served a year in jail. What a year! His folks wouldn't do a thing for him; they said such a thing had never happened ₁₀ in the family. And they let him take the consequences. (*He pauses.*) When he got out — (*stopping to correct himself*) when he was let out, his family offered him help. But he was too proud to accept the help; it hadn't been offered when he ₁₅ needed it most. He told his family that he never wanted to see them again. He changed his name so they couldn't find him. He left his home town. He came here.

THE GIRL. And he has been honest ever since! ₂₀

STRICKLAND. Ever since: for twenty-eight years! It was hard at times, terribly hard! In the beginning, when he had to go hungry and cold, when he saw other men riding around in carriages, he wondered if he hadn't made a mistake. He had ₂₅ knocked about a good deal; he had learned a lot, and he wouldn't have been caught so easily the second time. It was almost worth taking the chance! It was almost worth getting a foot of lead pipe, and waiting in some dark street — waiting, waiting for some sleek honest man with his pockets full of money! It would have been so simple! And he knew how! I don't know why he didn't do it.

THE GIRL. Tell me more.

STRICKLAND. He managed to live. It wasn't pleasant living; it wasn't even decent living. But he stayed alive! I don't like to think of what he did to stay alive: it was humiliating; it was shameful, because he hadn't been brought up to do that kind of thing, but it was honest. Honest; and when he walked home from his work at six o'clock, walked home to save the nickel, his betters never crowded him, because they didn't want to soil their clothes with his honest dirt! He had thought the year in jail was terrible. The first year he was free was worse. He had never been hungry in jail.

THE GIRL. Then his chance came.

STRICKLAND. Yes, it was a chance. He found a purse in the gutter, and he returned it to the owner before he had made up his mind whether to keep it or not. So they said he was honest! He knew he wasn't! He knew that he had returned it because there was so much money in it that he was afraid to keep it, but he never told them that. And when the man who owned the purse gave him a job, he worked — worked because he was afraid not to work; worked so that he wouldn't have any time to think; because he knew that, if he began to think, he would begin to steal! Then they said he was a hard worker, and they promoted him: they made him manager. That gave him 5 more chances to steal, but there were so many men watching him, so many men anxious for him to make a slip so that they might climb over him, that he didn't dare. (*He pauses.*)

THE GIRL. And then? 10

STRICKLAND. The rest was easy. Nothing succeeds like a good reputation, and he didn't steal because he knew they'd catch him. (*He pauses again.*) But he wasn't honest at bottom! The rotten streak was still there! After twenty-eight 15 years things began to be bad. He speculated — lost all the money he could call his own — and he made up his mind to take other money that wasn't his own — all he could lay his hands on — and run off with it! It was wrong! It was the work 20 of a lifetime gone. But it was the rottenness in him coming to the surface! It was the thief he thought dead coming to life again!

THE GIRL (*after a pause*). What a pity!

STRICKLAND. He had been honest so long — he 25 had made other people think that he was honest so long that he had made himself think that he was honest!

THE GIRL. Was he wrong, Mr. Strickland?

The Magic Spear

STRICKLAND (*looking into her eyes; very quietly*).
I don't know what sent you — who sent you; but
you've come here to-night as I am running away.
You're too late. You can't stop me. Not even
5 the finger of God Himself could stop me! I've
gone too far. (*He goes on in a voice which is low,
but terrible in its earnestness.*) Here is money!
(*He pulls out his pocketbook.*) Hundreds of thousands of it, not a cent of it mine! And I'm stealing
10 it. Do you understand me? Stealing it! To-
morrow the firm will be bankrupt, and there'll be
a reward out for me. (*He smiles grimly, and bows.*)
Here, if you please, is your honest man! What
have you to say to him?

15 THE GIRL (*very quietly*). The man who has been
honest so long that he has made himself think that
he is honest can't steal!

STRICKLAND (*hoarsely*). You believe that?

THE GIRL (*opening her bag again*). I was left a
20 little money this week — only a few hundred dollars, hardly enough to bother you with. Will you
take care of it for me — Alfred Stevens?

STRICKLAND. Good Heavens! (*And, utterly un-
nerved, he collapses into a chair. There is a long
25 pause.*)

THE GIRL (*crossing slowly to the window, and
drawing aside the curtain*). Look! What a beautiful night! The thousands of sleeping houses!
The millions of shining stars! And the lights

68

One cannot say: "Here God ends; here Man begins."

beneath! And in the distance, how the stars and
the lights meet! So that one cannot say: "Here
God ends; here Man begins."

(*The telephone rings, harshly and shrilly; Strickland goes to the receiver.*) 5

STRICKLAND (*quietly*). Yes?... You're afraid
I'm going to miss the train?... Yes? Well,
I'm going to miss the train!... I'm going to
stay and face the music! (*Hysterically*) I'm an
honest man, d'ye hear me? I'm an honest man. 10
(*Furiously he pitches the telephone to the floor, and
stands panting, shivering, on the spot. From the
window a soft radiance beckons, and trembling in
every limb, putting out his hands as if to ward off
some unseen obstacle, he moves there slowly.*) Did 15
you hear what I told him? I'm going to make
good. I'm going to face the music! Because I'm
an honest man! An honest man!

(*He gasps, stops abruptly, and, in a sudden panic-
stricken movement, tears the curtains down. The* 20
*window is closed — has never been opened — but the
girl has vanished. And as Strickland, burying his
face in his hands, drops to his knees in awe, the curtain
falls.*)

THE BROWN WALLET

Stacy Aumonier

GILES MEIKLEJOHN was a beaten man. Huddled in the corner of a third-class railway carriage on the journey from Epsom to London, he sullenly reviewed the unfortunate series of episodes which had brought him into the position in which he found himself. Dogged by bad luck! . . . Thirty-seven years of age; married; a daughter ten years old; nothing attained; his debts exceeding his assets; and now — out of work!

He had tried, too. A little pampered in his upbringing; when the crisis came he had faced it manfully. When, during his very first year at Oxford, the news came of his father's bankruptcy and sudden death from heart failure, he immediately went up to town and sought a situation in any capacity. His mother had died many years previously, and his only sister was married to a missionary in Burma. His accomplishments at that time? Well, he could play cricket and squash rackets; he knew a smattering of Latin and a

---

Reprinted by permission of Doubleday, Page & Co.
LINE 1. **Giles:** pronounced jīlz.

smudge of French; he remembered a few dates in history, and he could add up and subtract (a little unreliably). He was good-looking, genial, and of excellent physique. He had no illusions about the difficulties which faced him. 5

His father had always been a kind of practical visionary. Connected with big insurance interests, he was a man of large horizons, profound knowledge, and great ideals. Around his sudden failure and death there had always clung an atmosphere of 10 mystery. That he had never expected to fail, and was unprepared for death a week before it happened, is certain. He had had plans for Giles which up to that time he had had no opportunity of putting into operation. The end must have been 15 cyclonic.

Through the intervention of friends, Giles obtained a situation as clerk in an insurance office, his wages amounting to fifteen shillings a week, a sum he had managed to live on. In the evening 20 he attended classes, and studied shorthand and typewriting. At first the freshness of this experience, aided by youth and good health, stimulated him. But as time went on he began to realize that he had chosen work for which he was utterly un- 25 suited. He worked hard but made no progress. He had not a mathematical mind; he was slow in

---

Line **4**. **illusions:** fancies.

the up-take. The chances of promotion were remote. The men around him seemed so quick and clever. At the end of two years he decided to resign and try something else. If only he had been
5 taught a profession! After leaving the insurance office he went through various experiences; working at a seedman's nursery, going round with a circus, attempting to get on the stage and failing, working his passage out to South Africa, more clerk-
10 ing, nearly dying from enteric through drinking polluted water, working on an ostrich farm, returning to England as a male nurse to a young man who was mentally deficient.

It was not till he met Minting that he achieved
15 any success at all. They started a press-cutting agency in two rooms in Bloomsbury. Minting was clever, and Giles borrowed fifty pounds (from whom we will explain later). Strangely enough the press-cutting agency was a success.
20 After the first six months they began to do well.

It was at that time that he met Eleanor. She was secretary to Sir Herbert Woolley, the well-known actor-manager, and she happened to call one day concerning the matter of press cuttings for her
25 employer. From the very first moment there was never any question on either side but that both he and she had met their fate. Neither had there

---

LINE **10.** **enteric:** an intestinal fever.

been an instant's regret on either side since. They
were completely devoted. With the business promising well, he married her within three months.
It is probable that if the business had not existed
he would have done the same. They went to 5
live in a tiny flat in Maida Vale, and a child was
born the following year.

A period of unclouded happiness followed.
There was no fortune to be made out of press cuttings, but a sufficient competence to keep Eleanor 10
and the child in reasonable comfort. Everything
progressed satisfactorily for three years. And
then one July morning the blow fell. At that time
he and Minting were keeping a junior clerk. Giles
and Eleanor had been away to the sea for a fort- 15
night's holiday. Minting was to go on the day of
their return. When Giles arrived at the office he
found the clerk alone. To his surprise he heard
that Minting had not been there himself for a
fortnight. He did not have long to wait to find 20
the solution of the mystery. The first hint came
in the discovery of a blank counterfeit. Minting
had withdrawn every penny of their small capital
and vanished.

Giles did not tell his wife. He made a desperate 25
effort to pull the concern together, but in vain.
There was a great number of outstanding debts,
and he had just nine shillings when he returned
from his holiday. He rushed around and managed

73

to borrow a pound or two here and there, sufficient
to buy food and pay off the clerk, but he quickly
foresaw that the crash was inevitable. He had not
the business acumen of Minting, and no one seemed
5 prepared to invest money in a bankrupt press-
cutting agency. In the midst of his troubles the
original source of the fifty pounds upon which he
started his business wrote peremptorily demanding
the money back. He went there and begged and
10 pleaded, but it was obvious that the "original
source" looked upon him as a waster and ne'er-do-
well.

He went bankrupt, and Eleanor had to be told.
She took it in just the way he knew she would take
15 it. She said:

"Never mind, darling. We'll soon get on our
feet again."

She had been a competent secretary, with a
knowledge of French, bookkeeping, shorthand, and
20 typewriting. She set to work and obtained a situation herself as secretary to the manager of a firm
of wall-paper manufacturers, housing the child
during the day with a friendly neighbor.

Giles was idle the whole of August. They gave
25 up the flat and went into lodgings. In September
he got work as a clerk to a stationer. His salary
was thirty shillings a week, a pound less than his

LINE **4.** **acumen:** cleverness.

74

wife was getting. He felt the situation bitterly.
Poor Eleanor! How he had let her down. When
he spoke about it, though, she only laughed and
said:

"If our troubles are never anything worse than 5
financial ones, darling, I shan't mind."

They continued to be only financial ones till the
following year when Eleanor became very ill. In
a desperate state Giles again approached the "original source." After suffering considerable recrim- 10
ination and bullying he managed to extract another ten pounds, which quickly vanished. It was
three months before Eleanor was well enough to
resume work, and during that time they lived in a
state of penury. Giles lived almost entirely on 15
tea and bread, and became much run down and very
thin. He pretended to Eleanor that he had had an
increase, and that he had a good lunch every day, so
that all the money he earned could be spent on her
and the baby. In the meantime he dissected des- 20
perately that grimmest of all social situations —
the unskilled labor market. If only he had been
taught to be a bootmaker, a plumber, or a house-
painter, he would have been better off. Manners
may make men, but they don't make money, and 25
one has to make money to live. He became en-
vious of his fellow clerks and shop assistants who

LINE 10. recrimination: blame.

had never tasted the luxurious diet of a public-school training. That he had brains he was fully aware, but they had never been trained in any special direction. His ability, moreover, was of
5 the kind that does not adapt itself to commercial ends. He had always had a great affection for his father, but he began to nurture a resentment against his memory. His father had treated him badly, bringing him up to a life of ease and assur-
10 ance and then deserting him.

It would be idle and not very interesting to trace the record of his experiences during the next years up to the time when we find him in the train on the way back from Epsom. It is a dreary story,
15 the record of a series of dull underpaid jobs, a few bright gleams of hope, even days and nights of complete happiness, then dull reactions, strain, worry, hunger, nervous fears, blunted ambitions, and thwarted desires. Through it all the only
20 thing that remained unalterably bright and inspiring was his wife's face. Not once did she flinch, not once did she lose hope. Her constant slogan: "Never mind, old darling, we'll soon be on our feet again," was ever in his ears, buoying him up through
25 the darkest hours.

And again he was out of work, again Eleanor was not well, and again he had been to the "original source."

The "original source" was his uncle, his father's

The Brown Wallet

brother. He was a thin, acid old gentleman, known in commercial circles as a money-maniac. Living alone in a large house at Epsom, with all kinds of telephonic connections with the city, he thought and dreamed of nothing at all but his mistress — money. Between him and Giles' father had always existed a venomous hatred, far more pronounced on the side of his uncle than of his father. It had dated back many years. When his father died and Giles appealed to his uncle, the gentleman appeared thoroughly to enjoy giving him five pounds as an excuse for a lecture and a subtly conveyed sneer at his father's character.

He was a very wealthy man, and he could easily have launched Giles into the world by putting him through the training for one of the professions, but he preferred to dole out niggardly little bits of charity and advice, and to boast that he himself was a self-made man who had had no special training.

"No," thought Giles, "but you have an instinct for making money. I haven't. You don't have to train a duck to swim."

Naturally, they very quickly quarreled, and his uncle seemed to rejoice in his failures. It was only in his most desperate positions that he appealed to him again.

LINE **13.** **subtly:** craftily.

77

The Magic Spear

Lying back in the dimly lighted railway carriage, he kept on visualizing his uncle's keen malevolent eyes, the thrust of the pointed chin. The acid tones of his voice echoed through his brain:

5 "It's quite time, my lad, you pulled yourself together. You ought to have made your fortune by now. Don't imagine I'm always going to help you."

Giles had humbled his pride for his wife and child's sake. He had spent the night at his uncle's, 10 and by exercising his utmost powers of cajolery, had managed to extort three pounds. Three pounds! and the rent overdue, bills pressing, his wife unwell and he — out of work. What was he going to do?

The train rumbled into Waterloo Station without 15 his arriving at any satisfactory answer. He pulled his bag out from under the seat, and stepped slowly out of the carriage.

As he walked along the platform, it suddenly occurred to him that he was feeling weak and ex-20 hausted. "I hope to God I'm not going to be ill," he thought.

The bag, which contained only his night things and a change of clothes, seemed unbearably heavy. A slight feeling of faintness came over him as he 25 passed the ticket-collector.

"I believe I shall have to have a cab," flashed through him.

LINE **10.** **cajolery:** persuasion.

The Brown Wallet

Two important-looking men got out of a taxi which had just driven up. Giles engaged it, and having given his address he stepped in and sank back exhausted on to the seat. It was very dark in the cab, and he lay huddled in the corner — a 5 beaten man. Everything appeared distant and dim, and unimportant. He had eaten hardly any lunch, and his uncle seemed to have arranged that he should leave his house just before dinner. It was late, and he was hungry and overwrought. 10

The cab turned a corner sharply, and Giles lurched and thrust his hand on to the other end of the seat to prevent himself from falling. As he did so his knuckles brushed against an object. Quite apathetically he felt to see what it was. He picked 15 it up and held it near the window. It was a brown leather wallet, with a circular brass lock. He regarded it dubiously, and for an instant hesitated whether he should tell the driver to go back to the station, the wallet presumably belonging to one of 20 those two important-looking men who had got out. But would it be possible to find them? By that time they would probably have gone off by train. No, the right thing to do was to give it up to the police, of course. 25

It was a fat wallet, and he sat there with it in his hand, ruminating. He wondered what it con-

---

LINE **15.** **apathetically:** dully. **18.** **dubiously:** doubtfully. **27.** **ruminating:** thinking.

tained. Quite easy just to have a squint, anyway.
He tried to slip the catch but it wouldn't open.
It was locked. It is difficult to determine the
extent to which this knowledge affected him. If
5 it had not been locked, Giles Meiklejohn's immediate actions, and indeed his future career, might
have been entirely different. It irritated him that
the wallet was locked . . . tantalized him. If it
was locked, it meant that it contained something
10 . . . pretty useful. All around the park he lay
back in the cab, hugging the wallet like one in a
trance.

A desperate, beaten man, holding a fat wallet
in his hand. Contrary forces were struggling
15 within his tired mind. As he went up Park Lane,
one of these forces seemed to succumb to the other.
Almost in a dream he leaned out of the cab, and said
quietly to the driver: "Drive to the Trocadero.
I think I'll have a bit of supper first."

20 Arriving there, he paid the cabman, concealed
the wallet in his overcoat, and went in. He entered
a lavatory and locked himself in. With unruffled
deliberation he took out a penknife and began to
saw away at the leather around the lock.

25 "I just want to have a squint," he kept on mentally repeating.

It took him nearly a quarter of an hour to get the

LINE **18**. **Trocadero:** a London restaurant.

The Brown Wallet

wallet open, and when he did his heart was beating like a sledge hammer.

The wallet contained eight thick packets of one-pound treasury notes! He feverishly computed the number which each packet contained, and decided that it must be two thousand pounds' worth of ready cash in his possession!

A desperate, beaten man, with a wife and child, hungry . . . out of work . . . two thousand pounds! . . .

There seemed no question about it all then. One side of the scale was too heavily weighted. He took seventeen of the one-pound notes and put them in his pocketbook, the rest he divided into the pockets of his overcoat, where he also concealed the wallet. He went up into the bar and ordered a double brandy and soda. He drank it in two gulps and went out and hailed another taxi. On the way home he stopped at a caterer's, and bought a cold fowl, some pressed beef, new rolls, cheese, a box of chocolates, and a bottle of wine. Then he drove homeward.

Up to this point his actions seemed to have been controlled by some subconscious force. So far as his normal self was concerned, he had hardly thought at all. But as he began to approach his own neighborhood — his own wife — the realization of what he had done — what he was doing — came home to him.

"It was practically stealing. It is stealing, you know."

Yes, but what would any one else have done in that position? He couldn't let his wife and child ⁵starve. There was only one thing he was afraid of . . . his wife's eyes. She must never know. He would have to be cunning, circumspect. He must get rid of the wallet, conceal the notes from his wife — eke them out in driblets, pretend he was ¹⁰making money somehow. But the wallet? He couldn't leave it in the cab. It would be found and the cabman would give evidence. He mustn't drive home at all. He must get out again, think again. Between Paddington and Maida Vale ¹⁵runs a canal. Happy thought! a canal! He stopped at the bridge and dismissed the man, tipping him lavishly. The banks of the canal were railed off. It was possible to get near enough to throw something in only on the bridge. Thither he ²⁰walked at a rapid stride. The feeling of exhaustion had passed. He was tingling with excitement. He looked eagerly about for a stone, and cursed these modern arrangements of wooden pavements. There were no stones near the canal. Never mind, ²⁵the thing would probably sink. If it didn't, who could trace its discovery to his action? The point was to get rid of it unseen.

LINE **7.** **circumspect:** discreet; careful.

The Brown Wallet

He reached the bridge. A few stray people were passing backward and forward — must wait till every one was out of sight. He hung about, gripping his portmanteau in one hand, and the wallet in his right-hand overcoat pocket. He crossed the bridge once, but still seeing dark figures about, he had to return. Why not throw it now? No, there was some one watching in the road opposite — might be a policeman. The police, never had cause to feel frightened at the police before. There would be a splash. Some one might come out of the darkness, a deep voice:

"What was that you threw in the canal?"

No, no, couldn't do it. The bridge was too exposed, too much of a fairway. He hurried off, walking rapidly down side streets in the direction of his home. At last an opportunity presented itself. Shabby, deserted little street, a low stone wall enclosing a meager garden. Not a soul in sight. Like a flash he slipped the wallet over the wall and dropped it. Instantaneously he looked up at the house connected with the garden. A man was looking out of the first-floor window, watching him!

He turned and walked quickly back. He thought he heard a call. At the first turning he ran, the portmanteau banging against his leg and

LINE **4. portmanteau:** hand bag.   **15. fairway:** open stretch of ground.

impeding his progress. He ceased running only because people stopped and looked at him suspiciously.

"It's all right! It's all right!" he kept saying to
5 himself. "I've got rid of it."

Yes, he was rid of that danger, but there loomed before him the more insidious difficulty of concealing the notes. His pockets bulged with them. When he arrived home, Eleanor would run out
10 into the landing and throw her arms round him. He could almost hear the tones of her gentle voice saying:

"Whatever have you got in your pockets, darling?"

15 If he put them in the portmanteau, she would be almost certain to open it, or she would be in the room when he went to unpack. Very difficult to conceal anything from Eleanor; she knew all about him; every little thing about him interested
20 her. Nothing in their rooms was locked up. Moreover, she was very observant, methodical, and practical. Some one had called her psychic, but this was only because she thought more quickly than most people, and had unerring intuitions.

25 Giles would have to be very cunning. His mental energies were so concerned with the necessity for deceiving Eleanor that the moral aspect of

---

LINE 7. insidious: sly.

his position was temporarily blurred. He plunged
on through the darkness, his mind working rapidly.
At the corner of their meager street he was tempted
to stuff the notes in a pillar box and hurry home.

"Don't be a fool," said the other voice. "Here
are comfort and luxury interminably — not only for
yourself, for the others."

He went boldly up to the house and let himself
in. He heard other lodgers talking in the front
ground-floor room. He hurried by and reached
his own landing. To his relief Eleanor's voice
came from the room above:

"Is that you, darling?"

He dumped the bag down and in a flash had
removed his overcoat and hung it on a peg in a dark
corner. Then he called out:

"Hullo, old girl. Everything all right?"

Within a minute his wife's arms were around him,
and he exclaimed with forced triumph:

"I touched the old boy for twenty pounds!
I've brought home a chicken and things."

"Oh! how splendid! A chicken! Rather extravagant, isn't it, darling?"

"One must live, dear angel."

Her confidence and trust in him, her almost
childish glee over the gay feast, her solicitude in
his welfare, her anxiety that little Anna should
have some chicken, but keep the sweets till the
morrow, her voice later crooning over the child —

all these things mocked his conscience. But he couldn't afford to have a conscience. He couldn't afford to say:

"I stole all this and more."

5 He was eager for the attainment of that last instance — crooning over the child. While she was putting the little girl to bed, he crept out into the passage and extracted the packets of notes from his overcoat pocket. He took them into the
10 sitting room and wrapped them up in brown paper. He wrote on the outside, "stationery." Then he stuffed the parcel at the back of a cupboard where they kept all kinds of odds and ends.

"That'll have to do for to-night," he thought.
15 "I'm too tired to think of anything better."

When she came down he enlarged the claims of his exhaustion. He had a bit of a head, he explained; just as well to turn in early. In the darkness he clung to her fearfully, like a child in terror
20 of separation.

It was not till she was sleeping peacefully that the enormity of his offense came home to him.

If he were found out! It would kill her.

He remembered her expression:

25 "If our troubles are never anything worse than financial ones, darling, I shan't mind."

Good God! What had he done? He could

LINE **17.** **a bit of a head:** a slight headache.

call it what he liked, but, crudely speaking, it was just stealing. He had stolen. He was a criminal, a felon. If he should be found out, it meant arrest, trial, imprisonment — all these horrors he had only vaguely envisaged as concerning a different type of person from himself. In the rough and tumble of his life he had never before done anything criminal, never anything even remotely dishonest. And she, Eleanor, what would she think of him? It would destroy her love, destroy her life, ruin the child.

He must get up, go into the other room and — what? What could he do with the notes? Burn them? Eleanor had that mother's curious faculty for profound, but at the same time, watchful sleep. If he got out of bed, she would be aware of it. If he went into the next room and began burning things, she would be instantly alert.

"What's that burning, darling?"

An ever-loving wife may be an embarrassment when one is not quite playing the game. By destroying the wallet he had burnt his boats. If he returned the money, he would have to explain what the wallet was doing in a neighbor's garden with the brass lock cut away.

"Besides, you've already spent some," interjected that other voice. "You're horribly in debt. Here's succor. The money probably belongs to

---

Line **27.** **succor:** help.

The Magic Spear

some rich corporation. It's not like taking it from the poor. Don't be a fool. Go to sleep."

For hours he tossed feverishly, the pendulum of his resolutions swinging backward and forward. If he were to keep the money, he would have to invent some imaginary source of income, a fictitious job, perhaps, and that would be very difficult because Eleanor was so solicitous, such a glutton for details concerning himself. He might have made out that his uncle had given him a much larger sum of money, but in that case there was the danger that, in her impetuous manner, Eleanor might write to the old man, and the old man would smell a rat. Doubtless the affair of the lost wallet would be in the papers the next day, and wouldn't the old man be delighted to bring it home to Giles!

There was nothing to do but to trust to fate. The milk carts were clattering in the road before he slept.

It was hours later that he heard Anna's merry little laugh, and his wife's voice saying:

"Hush, darling, daddy's asleep. He's very tired."

He got up and faced the ordeals of the day. The place at the back of the lumber cupboard seemed the most exposed in the world. He racked his brains for a more suitable spot. But in whatever place he thought of, danger seemed to lurk. One never quite knew what Eleanor might do. She was so keen on tidying up and clearing things out. He decided that a crisp walk might clear his mind. He made up the excuse that he was going to the public library to look through the advertisements 5 and went out. He meant to smuggle the parcel of notes out with him, but Eleanor was too much on the spot. She helped him on with his overcoat and said :

"It'll soon be all right again, darling." 10

Poor Eleanor ! What a capacity she had for living ! She ought to have married a rich, successful, and clever man. She ought to have everything a beautiful woman desires. Well? . . . He walked quickly to the nearest news agent and bought a 15 paper. There was nothing in the morning paper about the loss of the wallet. He felt annoyed about this, until he realized that of course there wouldn't have been time. It would come out later. And indeed while he was standing on the curb anxiously 20 scrutinizing his morning paper, boys came along the street selling the *Star* and the *Evening News*.

A paragraph in the *Star*, headed "£2,000 left in a taxi," supplied him with the information he needed. It announced that Sir James Cusping, K. B. E., a 25 director of a well-known bank, and a chief cashier left a wallet containing two thousand pounds in

---

LINE **25**. **K. B. E.:** Knight of the British Empire.

treasury notes in a taxi at Waterloo Station. The money was the result of a cash transaction concerning certain bank investments. Any one giving information likely to lead to recovery would be
5 suitably rewarded. It also announced that Scotland Yard had the matter in hand.

So far the information was satisfactory. Sir James Cusping was a notoriously wealthy man, and the chief cashier was hardly likely to be held seri-
10 ously responsible for a loss for which such an important person was jointly responsible. The bank mentioned was a bank that advertised that its available assets exceeded four hundred million pounds. Two thousand pounds meant less to it
15 than two pence would mean to Giles. No one was hurt by the transfer of this useful sum to his own pocket. The sun was shining. Why be down in the mouth about it? What he had done he had done, and he must see it through.

20 How could anybody trace the theft to him? The two cabmen? They would be hardly likely to remember his face, and neither of them had driven him home. There was no danger from any one except Eleanor. A sudden fever of dread came
25 over him. She would assuredly turn out that cupboard to-day, find the packet of "stationery." Then — what?

LINE **5.** **Scotland Yard:** British detective service.

The Brown Wallet

He hurried back home. As he approached the house, other fears assailed him. He had visions of policemen waiting for him on the other side of the hall door.

His nerves were going to pot. He opened the door with exaggerated nonchalance. There was no one there. Eleanor was singing. The kettle was on the gas ring, ready for tea.

"What a cad I am to her," he thought.

The condition of frenzied agitation continued until the following afternoon; then it reached a crisis. He was feeling all unstrung. Seated alone in their little sitting room, he was struggling with the resolution to confess everything to Eleanor, when she entered the room. He glanced at her and nearly screamed. She was holding up the parcel in her hand!

In her cheerful voice she said:

"What is this parcel marked stationery, darling? I was turning out the cupboard."

Like an animal driven to bay he jumped up and almost snatched it from her. The inspiration of despair prompted him to exclaim:

"Oh! . . . that! Yes, yes, I wanted that. It's something a chap wanted me to get for him. . . . It doesn't belong to me."

A chap! What chap? Giles didn't usually

LINE **6. nonchalance:** indifference.

91

refer to chaps. They had no secrets apart. She looked surprised.

"I was just going to open it. As a matter of fact, we have run out of stationery."

5 "Eh? No, no, not that. I must send that back. I'll get some more stationery."

He tucked the packet under his arm and went out into the hall.

"You're not going out at once?" said Eleanor, 10 following.

"Yes, yes, I must post it at once. I'd quite forgotten."

He slipped on his coat and went out without his customary embrace.

15 Beads of perspiration were on his brow.

"That's done it!" He muttered in the street, "I must never take it back."

An extravagant plan formed in his mind. He went into the library and looked at the advertise-20 ments in a local paper. He took down some addresses in St. John's Wood. In half an hour's time he was calling on a landlady in a mean street.

"You have a furnished room to let?" he said when she appeared.

25 "Yes, sir."

"Well, it's like this. I am an author. I want a quiet room to work in during the daytime."

"I've got a nice room as would suit you."

"Come on, then, let me see it, please."

He booked the room, a shabby little overcrowded apartment.

"I'll be coming in to-day," he said.

"Very good, sir. What name might it be?"

"Er — name? Oh, yes, my name — er — John Parsons."

He fled down the street and sought a furnishing establishment.

"I want an oak desk which I can lock up — a good strong lock."

He paid seven pounds ten for the desk, and got it taken round at once on a barrow. He then bought scribbling papers, paper, and ink. He established himself in his room, stuffed the packet of notes in the desk, and locked it. Then he went out into the street again. The fresh air fanned his temples. He almost chuckled.

"Heavens! Why didn't I think of this at first?" he reflected. "After the life I've led one forgets the power of money."

He felt singularly calm and confident. It was dark when he got home. He kissed Eleanor and made up an elaborate story about a fellow clerk named Lyel Bristowe, who used to work in the same office, and whom he had met in the street recently. He had wanted this particular stationery most particularly. He had been to see him, and Bristowe was giving him an introduction to a man who might be able to offer him a good situation.

The story went down reasonably well, but he thought he detected a pucker of suspicion about his wife's brow.

He was too involved now to turn back. The following day he visited his furnished room. He anxiously unlocked the desk, took out the notes, examined them, put them back, took them out again, stuffed them in his pocket. . . . Very dangerous, after all, leaving them there; a flimsy lock . . . there might be a burglary. He had told the landlady he was an author, and it is true that he spent a great portion of the day inventing fiction . . . lies to tell Eleanor. He eventually locked the notes up again and went home.

He assumed a somewhat forced air of triumph. He had been successful. Through the influence of Bristowe he had secured a position as chief cashier to a firm of surgical instrument makers in Camden Town. His salary was to be five pounds a week to commence. Eleanor clapped her hands.

"Oh, but how lovely, darling! I suppose you can do it? You're such an old silly at figures."

He explained that the work was quite simple, and added ironically that the great thing Messrs. Binns and Binns wanted was a man they could trust.

Then the narrow life of lies proceeded apace. Every day he went to his room, fingered the notes, took some when he needed them, deliberately

invented the names and characters of his fellow
workers at Messrs. Binns and Binns, even made
up little incidents and stories concerning his daily
experiences. The whole affair was so inordinately
successful. No further reference was made in the 5
newspapers to the missing wallet, and though
Scotland Yard were supposed to have the matter
in hand, what could they do? Even if by chance
suspicion fell on him, there was nothing incrimi-
nating to be found in his lodgings, and not a soul 10
knew the whereabouts of "John Parsons." His
wife and child were living comfortably. He was
gradually paying off his debts.

But if the purely material side of his adventure
was successful, the same cannot be said of the 15
spiritual. He was tortured beyond endurance.
Lies bred lies. The moral lapse bred other moral
lapses. He was conscious of his own moral degen-
eration. He was ashamed to look his wife in the
face. In the evening, when he intended to be gay 20
and cheerful, he sat morosely in the corner, wishing
that the night would come — and go. In the daytime he would sit in his room, fretful and desolate.
In the mood of despair he began to set down his
experiences in terms of fiction, ascribing his feelings 25
to an imaginary person. Sometimes when the
position became unbearable he would go out and
drink. Often he would go up to the West End and
lunch extravagantly at some obscure restaurant.

95

The Magic Spear

He came into touch with unsavory people of the underworld.

The marks of his deterioration quickly became apparent to his wife.   One morning she said :

5 "Darling, you're working too hard at that place."

Then she wept a little, a thing she had never done in their days of adversity.   He swore that the work was not hard; the firm were very pleased with him and were going to give him a raise.

10 The weeks and months went by and he struggled to keep straight.   But little by little he felt himself slipping back.   He managed to write a few things which he sent off to publishers, but for the most part he avoided his room for any length of time, 15 and sat about in obscure cafés in Soho, drinking and playing cards.

Between himself and his wife the great chasm seemed to be yawning.   She was to him the dearest treasure in the world, and he was thrusting 20 her away.   In that one weak moment he had destroyed all chance of happiness — hers and his. Too late! Too late! In six months' time he found that he had spent nearly five hundred pounds! At this rate in another eighteen months 25 it would all be gone, and then — what? His moral character destroyed, his wife broken in health, the child without protection or prospects.

LINE **1**. **unsavory:** unpleasant.   **15**. **Soho:** a part of London.

The Brown Wallet

One morning he observed his wife glancing in the mirror as she did her hair. It came home to him abruptly that she had aged, aged many years in the last six months. Soon she would be turning gray, middle-aged, old-aged. And he? His hair was 5 thin on top, his face flabby, his nerves eternally on edge. Sometimes he was rude and snappy to her. And he buried his face in the pillow and thought:

"Oh, my darling, what have I done? What have 10 I done?"

That day he concentrated on a great resolve. This thing would have to stop. He would rather be a starving clerk again, rather a bricklayer's navvy, a crossing-sweeper, anything. He wandered 15 about the streets, hugging his determination. He avoided his old haunts. There must be no compromise. The thing should be cut clean out. He would confess. They would send back the remainder of the money anonymously, and start all 20 over. It was hard, but anything was better than this torture.

He returned home early in the afternoon, his face pale and tense. His wife was on the landing. She said: 25

"Oh, I was just going to send a telegram on to

Line **15.** **navvy:** a laborer.   **20.** **anonymously:** without giving a name.

97

you. It's from your uncle. He says come at
once."

A queer little stab of the old instinct of conspiracy
went through him. If she had sent the telegram on,
5 it would have come back : "No such firm known at
this address."

What did his uncle want? Come at once?
Should he go, or should he make his confession
first?

10 "I think you ought to go, darling. It sounds
important."

Very well, then. The confession should be
postponed till his return.

He caught a train at a quarter to four, and
15 arrived at his uncle's house in daylight. An old
housekeeper let him in and said :

"Ah! Your uncle's been asking for you. The
doctor's here."

"Is he ill?"

20 "They say he hasn't long to live. The poor man
is in great agony."

He was kept waiting ten minutes. A doctor
came out to him, looking very solemn.

"I've just given him an injection of strychnine.
25 He wishes to see you alone."

His uncle was propped up against the pillows.
His face was unrecognizable except for the eyes,

Line **24.** **strychnine:** a stimulating drug.

which were unnaturally bright.   Giles went close up
to him, and took his hand.   The old man's voice
was only just audible.   He whispered :

"Quickly ! quickly ! I shall be going —"

"What is it, uncle ?"   5

"It mustn't come out, see?   mustn't get into
the newspapers, nothing, the disgrace, see ?   That's

His face was unrecognizable except for the eyes, which were
unnaturally bright.

why . . . no checks must pass; all cash transaction, see ?"

"What do you want me to do ?"   10

"On that bureau . . . a brown paper parcel
. . . it's yours, all in bonds and cash, see ?
Twenty-eight thousand pounds . . . it really belongs to your father . . . I can't explain . . . I'm
going. He — I swindled him . . . he thought 15

he was . . . it's all through me he . . . bankrupt, death, see?"

"Do you mean my father . . . killed himself?"

"Not exactly, see? Hastened his end . . .
5 thought he would get into trouble. Take it, Giles, for God's sake. Let me die in peace."

"Why did you? Why did you?"

"I loved your mother . . . take it, Giles, for God's sake. Oh, this pain! . . . it's coming . . .
10 God help me!"

It was very late when Giles arrived home. His wife was asleep in bed. All the way home he had been repeating to himself in a dazed way.

"Twenty-eight thousand pounds. No, twenty-
15 six thousand. Two thousand to be sent back anonymously to the bank. No need for confession. Twenty-six thousand pounds. Eleanor, Anna. Oh, my dears!"

On the table in the sitting room was a letter
20 from a firm of publishers, addressed to Mr. John Parsons. It stated that the firm considered the short novel submitted to be a work of striking promise, and the manager would be glad if Mr. Parsons would call on them.

25 "Perhaps I've found out what I can do," Giles meditated.

Eleanor came into the room in her dressing gown and embraced him.

"All right, darling?"

The Brown Wallet

"Very much. Uncle has given me twenty-eight — I mean twenty-six thousand pounds. He said he cheated my father out of it."

"Darling! Cheated! How awful."

No, there was no need for confession. The sudden wild change in their fortunes got into his blood. He gripped her round the waist and lifted her up.

"Think of it, old girl, money to live on for ever. A place in the country, eh? You know, your dream: a bit of land and an old house, flowers, chickens, dogs, books, a pony perhaps. What about it?"

"Oh, Giles, I can't realize it. But how splendid, too, about the publishers' letter. Why didn't you tell me you were writing? Why do you call yourself John Parsons?"

In the silent night he told her everything.

It was Eleanor's hand which printed in Roman lettering on the outside of a parcel the address of Sir James Cusping, K.B.E. Inside were two thousand pounds in treasury notes, and on a slip of paper in the same handwriting: "Conscience money. Found in a taxi."

RICHARD CONFESSES

George Meredith

A LITTLE laurel-shaded temple of white marble
looked out on the river from a knoll bordering the
Raynham beechwoods, and was dubbed by Adrian
Daphne's Bower.   To this spot Richard had retired,

He allowed Austin to greet him and sit by him without lifting
his head.

5 and there Austin found him with his head buried
in his hands, a picture of desperation, whose last
shift has been defeated.   He allowed Austin to greet

Reprinted from George Meredith's *The Ordeal of Richard
Feverel*, published by Charles Scribner's Sons.

him and sit by him without lifting his head. Perhaps his eyes were not presentable.

"Where's your friend?" Austin began.

"Gone!" was the answer, sounding cavernous from behind hair and fingers. An explanation presently followed, that a summons had come for him in the morning from Mr. Thompson; and that Mr. Ripton had departed against his will.

In fact, Ripton had protested that he would defy his parent and remain by his friend in the hour of adversity and at the post of danger. Sir Austin signified his opinion that a boy should obey his parent, by giving orders to Benson for Ripton's box to be packed and ready before noon; and Ripton's alacrity in taking the baronet's view of filial duty was as little feigned as his offer to Richard to throw filial duty to the winds. He rejoiced that the Fates had agreed to remove him from the very hot neighborhood of Lobourne, while he grieved, like an honest lad, to see his comrade left to face calamity alone. The boys parted amicably, as they could hardly fail to do, when Ripton had sworn fealty to the Feverels with a warmth that made him declare himself bond, and due to appear at any stated hour and at any stated place to fight all the farmers in England, on a mandate from the heir of the house.

"So you're left alone," said Austin, contemplating the boy's shapely head. "I'm glad of it. We

never know what's in us till we stand by ourselves."

There appeared to be no answer forthcoming.
Vanity, however, replied at last, "He wasn't much
5 support."

"Remember his good points now he's gone,
Ricky."

"Oh! he was stanch," the boy grumbled.

"And a stanch friend is not always to be found.
10 Now, have you tried your own way of rectifying
this business, Ricky?"

"I have done everything."

"And failed!"

There was a pause, and then the deep-toned
15 evasion —

"Tom Bakewell's a coward!"

"I suppose, poor fellow," said Austin, in his kind
way, "he doesn't want to get into a deeper mess.
I don't think he's a coward."

20 "He is a coward," cried Richard. "Do you
think if I had a file I would stay in prison? I'd
be out the first night! And he might have had
the rope, too — a rope thick enough for a couple of
men his size and weight. Ripton and I and Ned
25 Markham swung on it for an hour, and it didn't
give way. He's a coward, and deserves his fate.
I've no compassion for a coward."

"Nor I much," said Austin.

Richard had raised his head in the heat of his

denunciation of poor Tom. He would have hidden
it had he known the thought in Austin's clear eyes
while he faced them.

"I never met a coward myself," Austin continued.
"I have heard of one or two. One let an innocent
man die for him."

"How base!" exclaimed the boy.

"Yes, it was bad," Austin acquiesced.

"Bad!" Richard scorned the poor contempt.
"How I would have spurned him! He was a
coward!"

"I believe he pleaded the feelings of his family in
his excuse, and tried every means to get the man off.
I have read also in the confessions of a celebrated
philosopher that in his youth he committed some
act of pilfering, and accused a young servant girl
of his own theft, who was condemned and dismissed
for it, pardoning her guilty accuser."

"What a coward!" shouted Richard. "And he
confessed it publicly?"

"You may read it yourself."

"He actually wrote it down, and printed it?"

"You have the book in your father's library.
Would you have done so much?"

Richard faltered. No! he admitted that he
never could have told people.

"Then who is to call that man a coward?" said

Line **8.** **acquiesced:** agreed.

Austin. "He expiated his cowardice as all who give way in moments of weakness, and are not cowards, must do. The coward chooses to think, 'God does not see. I shall escape.' He who is 5 not a coward, and has succumbed, knows that God has seen all, and it is not so hard a task for him to make his heart bare to the world. Worse, I should fancy it, to know myself an impostor when men praised me."

10 Young Richard's eyes were wandering on Austin's gravely cheerful face. A keen intentness suddenly fixed them, and he dropped his head.

"So I think you're wrong, Ricky, in calling this poor Tom a coward because he refuses to try your 15 means of escape," Austin resumed. "A coward hardly objects to drag in his accomplice. And, where the person involved belongs to a great family, it seems to me that for a poor plow lad to volunteer not to do so speaks him anything but a 20 coward."

Richard was dumb. Altogether to surrender his rope and file was a fearful sacrifice, after all the time, trepidation, and study he had spent on those two saving instruments. If he avowed Tom's 25 manly behavior, Richard Feverel was in a totally new position. Whereas, by keeping Tom a coward, Richard Feverel was the injured one, and to seem

---

LINE 1. **expiated:** atoned for. **5. succumbed:** yielded. **23. trepidation:** fearful agitation.

injured is always a luxury; sometimes a necessity, whether among boys or men.

In Austin the Magian conflict would not have lasted long. He had but a blind notion of the fierceness with which it raged in young Richard. 5 Happily for the boy, Austin was not a preacher. A single instance, a cant phrase, a fatherly manner, might have wrecked him, by arousing ancient or latent opposition. The born preacher we feel instinctively to be our foe. He may do some good 10 to the wretches that have been struck down and lie gasping on the battlefield; he rouses antagonism in the strong. Richard's nature, left to itself, wanted little more than an indication of the proper track, and when he said, "Tell me what I can do, 15 Austin," he had fought the best half of the battle. His voice was subdued. Austin put his hand on the boy's shoulder.

"You must go down to Farmer Blaize."

"Well!" said Richard, sullenly divining the deed 20 of penance.

"You'll know what to say to him when you're there."

The boy bit his lip and frowned. "Ask a favor of that big brute, Austin? I can't!" 25

"Just tell him the whole case, and that you don't

LINE **3. Magian:** learned; difficult. This word derives from the Magi or Wise Men. **9. latent:** hidden.

The Magic Spear

intend to stand by and let the poor fellow suffer without a friend to help him out of his scrape."

"But, Austin," the boy pleaded, "I shall have to ask him to help off Tom Bakewell! How can I ⁵ ask him, when I hate him?"

Austin bade him go, and think nothing of the consequences till he got there.

Richard groaned in soul.

"You've no pride, Austin."

¹⁰ "Perhaps not."

"You don't know what it is to ask a favor of a brute you hate."

Richard stuck to that view of the case, and stuck to it the faster, the more imperatively the urgency ¹⁵ of a movement dawned upon him.

"Why," continued the boy, "I shall hardly be able to keep my fists off him!"

"Surely you've punished him enough, boy?" said Austin.

²⁰ "He struck me!" Richard's lip quivered. "He dared not come at me with his hands. He struck me with a whip. He'll be telling everybody that he horsewhipped me, and that I went down and begged his pardon! A Feverel beg his pardon! Oh, if I ²⁵ had my will!"

"The man earns his bread, Ricky. You poached on his grounds. He turned you off, and you fired his rick."

LINE **14. urgency:** necessity.

108

"And I'll pay him for his loss. And I won't do any more."

"Because you won't ask a favor of him?"

"No! I will not ask a favor of him."

Austin looked at the boy steadily. "You prefer to receive a favor from poor Tom Bakewell?"

At Austin's enunciation of this obverse view of the matter Richard raised his brow. Dimly a new light broke in upon him. "Favor from Tom Bakewell, the plowman? How do you mean, Austin?"

"To save yourself an unpleasantness, you permit a country lad to sacrifice himself for you? I confess I should not have so much pride."

"Pride!" shouted Richard, stung by the taunt, and set his sight hard at the blue ridges of the hills.

Not knowing for the moment what else to do, Austin drew a picture of Tom in prison, and repeated Tom's volunteer statement. The picture, though his intentions were far from designing it so, had to Richard, whose perception of humor was infinitely keener, a horrible chawbacon smack about it. Visions of a grinning lout, open from ear to ear, unkempt, coarse, splay-footed, rose before him and afflicted him with the strangest sensations of disgust and comicality, mixed up with pity and

---

LINE **7.** **obverse:** opposite; on the other side. **23.** **lout:** a rough country fellow. **24.** **splay-footed:** with a foot flattened and spread out.

remorse — a sort of twisted pathos. There lay
Tom; hob-nail Tom! a bacon-munching, reckless,
beer-swilling animal! and yet a man; a dear brave
human heart notwithstanding; capable of devotion
5 and unselfishness. The boy's better spirit was
touched, and it kindled his imagination to realize
the abject figure of poor clodpole Tom, and surround
it with a halo of mournful light. His soul was alive.
Feelings he had never known streamed in upon him
10 as from an ethereal casement, an unwonted tenderness, an embracing humor, a consciousness of some
ineffable glory, an irradiation of the features of
humanity. All this was in the bosom of the boy,
and through it all the vision of an actual hob-nail
15 Tom, coarse, unkempt, open from ear to ear; whose
presence was a finger of shame to him and an
oppression of clodpole; yet toward whom he felt
just then a loving-kindness beyond what he felt
for any living creature. He laughed at him and
20 wept over him. He prized him, while he shrank
from him. It was a genial strife of the angel in
him with constituents less divine; but the angel
was uppermost and led the van, extinguishing
loathing, humanized laughter, transfigured pride
25 — pride that would persistently contemplate the
corduroys of gaping Tom, and cry to Richard, in

LINE **10.** **ethereal:** heavenly. **casement:** window.
12. ineffable: unspeakable. **22. constituents:** elements.

the very tone of Adrian's ironic voice, "Behold your benefactor!"

Austin sat by the boy, unaware of the sublimer tumult he had stirred. Little of it was perceptible in Richard's countenance. The lines of his mouth 5 were slightly drawn; his eyes hard set into the distance. He remained thus many minutes. Finally he jumped to his legs, saying, "I'll go at once to old Blaize and tell him."

Austin grasped his hand, and together they issued 1c out of Daphne's Bower, in the direction of Lobourne.

CAPE HORN

Herman Melville

ERE the calm had yet left us, a sail had been
discerned from the fore-topmast-head, at a great
distance, probably three leagues or more. At
first it was a mere speck, altogether out of sight
5 from the deck. By the force of attraction, or
something else equally inscrutable, two ships in
a calm, and equally affected by the currents, will
always approximate, more or less. Though there
was not a breath of wind, it was not a great while
10 before the strange sail was descried from our
bulwarks; gradually, it drew still nearer.

What was she, and whence? There is no object
which so excites interest and conjecture, and, at
the same time baffles both, as a sail, seen as a mere
15 speck on these remote seas off Cape Horn.

A breeze! A breeze! for lo! the stranger is
now perceptibly nearing the frigate; the officer's
spyglass pronounces her a full-rigged ship, with
all sail set, and coming right down to us, though
20 in our own vicinity the calm still reigns.

LINE **6.** **inscrutable :** difficult to understand. **8. approxi-**
mate : approach.

Cape Horn

She is bringing the wind with her. Hurrah! Ay, there it is! Behold how mincingly it creeps over the sea, just ruffling and crisping it.

Our topmen were at once sent aloft to loose the sails, and presently they faintly began to distend. As yet we hardly had steerageway. Toward sunset the stranger bore down before the wind, a complete pyramid of canvas. Never before, I venture to say, was Cape Horn so audaciously insulted. Stunsails alow and aloft; royals, moonsails, and everything else. She glided under our stern, within hailing distance, and the signal quartermaster ran up our ensign to the gaff.

"Ship ahoy!" cried the lieutenant of the watch, through his trumpet.

"Halloa!" bawled an old fellow in a green jacket, clapping one hand to his mouth, while he held on with the other in the mizzen shrouds.

"What ship's that?"

"The *Sultan*, Indiaman, from New York, and bound to Callao and Canton, sixty days out, all well. What frigate's that?"

"The United States ship *Neversink*, homeward bound."

LINE **6.** **steerageway:** that degree of forward movement of a ship which makes her governable by the helm. **9. audaciously:** daringly. **13. gaff:** a spar for extending the edge of certain sails. **18. mizzen shrouds:** part of a ship's rigging.

The Magic Spear

"Hurrah! hurrah! hurrah!" yelled our enthusiastic countryman, transported with patriotism.

By this time the *Sultan* had swept past, but the lieutenant of the watch could not withhold a
5 parting admonition.

"D'ye hear? You'd better take in some of your flying kites there. Look out for Cape Horn!"

But the friendly advice was lost in the now increasing wind. With a suddenness by no means
10 unusual in these latitudes, the light breeze soon became a succession of sharp squalls, and our sail-proud braggadocio of an Indiaman was observed to let everything go by the run, his t'gallant stunsails and flying jib taking quick leave of the
15 spars; the flying jib was swept into the air, rolled together for a few minutes, and tossed about in the squalls like a football. But the wind played no such pranks with the more prudently managed canvas of the *Neversink*, though before many
20 hours it was stirring times with us.

About midnight, when the starboard watch, to which I belonged, was below, the boatswain's whistle was heard, followed by the shrill cry of "All hands take in sail! Jump, men, and save
25 ship!"

---

12. braggadocio: braggart. **13. t'gallant stunsails:** upper auxiliary sails. **14. flying jib:** a triangular sail on an extended boom. **21. starboard:** right side of a ship. **watch:** group of men on duty for four hours.

Cape Horn

Springing from our hammocks, we found the frigate leaning over to it so steeply that it was with difficulty we could climb the ladders leading to the upper deck.

Here the scene was awful. The vessel seemed to 5 be sailing on her side. The main-deck guns had several days before been run in and housed, and the portholes closed, but the lee carronades on the quarter-deck and forecastle were plunging through the sea, which undulated over them in milk-white 10 billows of foam. With every lurch to leeward the yardarm ends seemed to dip in the sea, while forward the spray dashed over the bows in cataracts, and drenched the men who were on the foreyard. By this time the deck was alive with the whole 15 strength of the ship's company, five hundred men, officers and all, mostly clinging to the weather bulwarks. The occasional phosphorescence of the yeasting sea cast a glare upon their uplifted faces, as a night fire in a populous city lights up the panic- 20 stricken crowd.

In a sudden gale, or when a large quantity of sail is suddenly to be furled, it is the custom for the first lieutenant to take the trumpet from whoever happens then to be officer of the deck. 25 But Mad Jack had the trumpet that watch; nor did the first lieutenant now seek to wrest it from

LINE **11.** **leeward:** side opposite to that from which the wind comes.

his hands. Every eye was upon him, as if we had
chosen him from among us all, to decide this
battle with the elements, by single combat with the
spirit of the Cape; for Mad Jack was the saving
5 genius of the ship, and so proved himself that night.
I owe this right hand, that is this moment flying
over my sheet, and all my present being to Mad
Jack. The ship's bows were now butting, batter-
ing, ramming, and thundering over and upon the
10 head seas, and with a horrible wallowing sound our
whole hull was rolling in the trough of the foam.
The gale came athwart the deck and every sail
seemed bursting with its wild breath.

All the quartermasters and several of the fore-
15 castlemen were swarming round the double wheel
on the quarter-deck. Some jumping up and down,
with their hands upon the spokes; for the whole
helm and galvanized keel were fiercely feverish,
with the life imparted to them by the tempest.

20 "Hard UP the helm!" shouted Captain Claret,
bursting from his cabin like a ghost in his night-
dress.

"Damn you!" raged Mad Jack to the quartermasters; "hard DOWN — hard DOWN, I say,
25 and be damned to you!"

Contrary orders! but Mad Jack's were obeyed.
His object was to throw the ship into the wind,

LINE **18.** **galvanized:** energetic.

so as the better to admit of close-reefing the top-sails. But though the halyards were let go, it was impossible to clew down the yards, because of the enormous horizontal strain on the canvas. It now blew a hurricane. The spray flew over the ship in floods. The gigantic masts seemed about to snap under the world-wide strain of the three entire topsails.

"Clew down! clew down!" shouted Mad Jack, husky with excitement, and in a frenzy, beating his trumpet against one of the shrouds. But, owing to the slant of the ship, the thing could not be done. It was obvious that before many minutes something must go — either sails, rigging, or sticks; perhaps the hull itself, and all hands.

Presently a voice from the top exclaimed that there was a rent in the main topsail. And instantly we heard a report like two or three muskets discharged together; the vast sail was rent up and down like the Veil of the Temple. This saved the mainmast; for the yard was now clewed down with comparative ease, and the topmen lay out to stow the shattered canvas. Soon the two remaining topsails were also clewed down and close-reefed.

Above all the roar of the tempest and the shouts

LINE **2.** **halyards:** sail ropes. **20.** **Veil of the Temple:** the curtain which shut off the Holy of Holies in the Temple of Jerusalem.

of the crew, was heard the dismal tolling of the ship's
bell — almost as large as that of a village church —
which the violent rolling of the ship was occasioning.
Imagination cannot conceive the horror of such a
5 sound in a night tempest at sea.

"Stop that ghost!" roared Mad Jack; "away,
one of you, and wrench off the clapper!"

But no sooner was this ghost gagged, than a still
more appalling sound was heard, the rolling to and
10 fro of the heavy shot, which, on the gun deck,
had broken loose from the gun racks, and converted
that part of the ship into an immense bowling
alley.   Some hands were sent down to secure them;
but it was as much as their lives were worth.
15 Several were maimed; and the midshipmen who
were ordered to see the duty performed reported it
impossible, until the storm abated.

The most terrific job of all was to furl the mainsail, which, at the commencement of the squalls,
20 had been clewed up, coaxed, and quieted as much as
possible with the buntlines and slab lines.   Mad
Jack waited some time for a lull, ere he gave an
order so perilous to be executed.   For to furl this
enormous sail, in such a gale, required at least
25 fifty men on the yard; whose weight, superadded
to that of the ponderous stick itself, still further
jeopardized their lives.   But there was no prospect

Line **25.**   **yard:** crosswise spar.

of a cessation of the gale, and the order was at last given.

At this time a hurricane of slanting sleet and hail was descending upon us; the rigging was coated with a thin glare of ice, formed within the hour. 5

"Aloft, main-yardmen! and all you maintop-men! and furl the mainsail!" cried Mad Jack.

I dashed down my hat, slipped out of my quilted jacket in an instant, kicked the shoes from my feet, and, with a crowd of others, sprang for the rigging. 10 Above the bulwarks (which in a frigate are so high as to afford much protection to those on deck) the gale was horrible. The sheer force of the wind flattened us to the rigging as we ascended, and every hand seemed congealing to the icy shrouds 15 by which we held.

"Up — up, my brave hearties!" shouted Mad Jack; and up we got, some way or other, all of us, and groped our way out on the yardarms.

"Hold on, every mother's son!" cried an old 20 quarter gunner at my side. He was bawling at the top of his compass; but in the gale, he seemed to be whispering; and I heard him only from his being right to windward of me.

But his hint was unnecessary; I dug my nails 25 into the jackstays, and swore that nothing but death should part me and them until I was able to

---

LINE **22.** **compass:** voice range.

turn round and look to windward. As yet, this was impossible; I could scarcely hear the man to leeward at my elbow; the wind seemed to snatch the words from his mouth and fly away with them
5 into the south pole.

All this while the sail itself was flying about, sometimes catching over our heads, and threatening to tear us from the yard in spite of all our hugging. For about three quarters of an hour we thus hung
10 suspended right over the rampant billows, which curled their very crests under the feet of some four or five of us clinging to the lee yardarm, as if to float us from our place.

Presently, the word passed along the yard from
15 windward that we were ordered to come down and leave the sail to blow, since it could not be furled. A midshipman, it seemed, had been sent up by the officer of the deck to give the order, as no trumpet could be heard where we were.

20 Those on the weather yardarm managed to crawl upon the spar and scramble down the rigging; but with us, upon the extreme leeward side, this feat was out of the question; it was, literally, like climbing a precipice to get to windward in
25 order to reach the shrouds; besides, the entire yard was now incased in ice, and our hands and feet were so numb that we dared not trust our lives

---

LINE **25.** **shrouds:** ropes.

to them. Nevertheless, by assisting one another, we contrived to throw ourselves prostrate along the yard, and embrace it with our arms and legs. In this position, the stunsail booms greatly assisted in securing our hold. Strange as it may appear, I do not suppose that, at this moment, the slightest sensation of fear was felt by one man on that yard. We clung to it with might and main ; but this was instinct. The truth is that, in circumstances like these, the sense of fear is annihilated in the unutterable sights that fill all the eye and the sounds that fill all the ear. You become identified with the tempest ; your insignificance is lost in the riot of the stormy universe around.

Below us, our noble frigate seemed thrice its real length — a vast black wedge, opposing its widest end to the combined fury of the sea and wind.

At length the first fury of the gale began to abate, and we at once fell to pounding our hands, as a preliminary operation to going to work ; for a gang of men had now ascended to help secure what was left of the sail ; we somehow packed it away, at last, and came down.

About noon the next day, the gale so moderated that we shook two reefs out of the topsails, set new courses, and stood due east, with the wind astern.

Thus, all the fine weather we encountered after

first weighing anchor on the pleasant Spanish coast was but a prelude to this one terrific night; more especially, that treacherous calm immediately preceding it. But how could we reach our long-

We stood due east, with the wind astern.

5 promised homes without encountering Cape Horn? By what possibility avoid it? And though some ships have weathered it without these perils, yet by far the greater part must encounter them.

Cape Horn

Lucky it is that it comes about midway in the homeward-bound passage, so that the sailors have time to prepare for it, and time to recover from it after it is astern.

But, sailor, or landsman, there is some sort of ₅ Cape Horn for all. Boys! beware of it; prepare for it in time. Graybeards! thank God it is passed. And ye lucky livers, to whom, by some rare fatality, your Cape Horns are placid as Lake Lemans, flatter not yourselves that good luck is ₁₀ judgment and discretion; for all the yolk in your eggs, you might have foundered and gone down, had the Spirit of the Cape said the word.

LINE **9. placid:** calm.   **10. Lemans:** Lake Leman (lē'măn) is now called Lake Geneva.

THREE EYES

Wilfred T. Grenfell

"It's no good, master. If you don't go ahead
and break the path with your long legs, I can't go
a step farther" — and my beautiful leading dog
Snowball fairly sat down on her haunches and
5 faced me. It was her appealing eyes that spoke,
of course, but their "say-so" means more than any
amount of talk does. Truth to say, I was not
surprised, for the bottomless light snow had compelled us to walk ahead on our rackets since
10 dawn, the heavy sleigh had completely beaten out
the dogs, and we were all of us about "all in," as
they say on the Coast.

Bidding the team sit down, I climbed through the
wood on one side of the hill which we were skirting,
15 so as to try to make out our position. Soon, to
my infinite satisfaction, I found that we were on
the bluff of the sea cliffs, and that away below us the
sparkle of a small light was visible.

Reprinted from *Tales of the Labrador* by Wilfred T. Grenfell,
and used by permission of and by arrangement with Houghton
Mifflin Company, the authorized publishers.

LINE **9.** **rackets:** large soles on which one may be supported on snow; snowshoes.

Three Eyes

"Surely, that's Jerry Scanlan's cottage just below us, Snowball," I said on returning to the team. "Pull yourselves together for the last bit. We can almost roll on to it from the bluff."

Without a word of remonstrance, she uncurled [5] herself from the hole she had made in the snow, snapped out a call to the team, and waded off once more chest-high through the endless drift.

"A day's rest won't hurt 'em," said Jerry to me the next morning, as I stood on the porch receiving [10] the morning salutations of my dogs. "Nor you either," he added. "There be plenty of good herrin' for the dogs, and you and me can have a day's swatchin'" — which means trying to shoot old seals in the holes of water among the pack [15] ice.

"I'll give 'em two feeds to-day, if you'll stay," he went on, seeing me hesitate, "and they'll do two days' work in one to-morrow."

"There's more logic than there sounds in that," [20] I mused, as I noted how my dogs, well nourished when winter work began, now showed the anatomy of their ribs.

"Very well, feed 'em now, Jerry," I answered, which of course meant that you could not drive [25] them any more that day.

As we started out on the floe, I was surprised to find a large white, gray-whiskered dog, with a single rakish black patch over one eye, which had

earned him the sobriquet of "Three Eyes," following us. He had on his harness, with a long trace
trailing behind.

"Frighten the seals, won't he, Jerry?" I called
5 out, thinking he had not noticed the dog.

"Don't you believe it, Doctor. I wouldn't go
without him for fifty dollars."

After a long and unsuccessful day on the ice,
the wind being too much on shore, and the
10 "swatches," or open water, being mostly closed,
as we sat before the crackling log fire, I suddenly
became aware that the big white dog was stretched
out under the table. I had never seen a sledge
dog inside a house before.

15 "Is Three Eyes allowed in the house?" I asked;
"because he's under the table."

"That's his right, Doctor," said Jerry, "ever
since he saved my life."

You can generally tell something about a man
20 himself if you know his dog, and I was sure that if
Three Eyes was a reflection of Jerry, he was worth
closer acquaintance.

"Tell me something about the dog, Jerry. How
did he save your life?"

25 "I'm reckonin' he's done it more than once,
Doctor. He's a traveled dog, is Three Eyes.
He's been to France, too. One of them Frenchmen

LINE **1.** **sobriquet:** nickname.

that comes out in the summer fishin' heard about the dog, and one day I couldn't find him anywhere. After two or three days I started out to look for him, but he was nowhere to be found, and it wasn't till some of the ships had left that a man up and told me he'd seen Three Eyes on the *Belle Marie*, when he was aboard getting a bottle of wine for his wife. Brother Jim was just going south in our schooner for supplies, and I sent a telegram by him, to be sent to France to ask them to look out for the dog. Well, sir, I heard no more about it till one day about a year later, when in walks Three Eyes all by himself, waggin' his tail, as if he'd just been for a little walk around the house, instead of halfway round the world. A French captain told me after that the customs officer had seized the dog when the *Belle Marie* came to Havre and had sent him back by my old friend Captain Denis. The skipper had landed him about four miles from home as he passed along the Coast, and Three Eyes had just walked home by himself.

"Them was the days of my poverty, Doctor. Us had a hard family, six boys and four girls, and all small, too. The traders had it all their own way them times. Provisions was that high that us was on a dry diet more than once by New Year's. And clothin' — well, that was mostly beyond reach altogether. The only chance us had for fresh food before t' fish set in in June was seals

127

and ducks, and they don't come down till late in
April; so you may believe that Three Eyes knew
all about swiles. He'd dive down in three fathoms
o' water for a cent any time, and more than one
5 was the swile that he brought me up from the
bottom in t' fall before they gets fat enough to
float by theirselves. I've had many dogs in my
time — good dogs, mind you, too — but none
quite like Three Eyes. If you loses your way in
10 a blizzard, you can just leave it to Three Eyes,
and he'll take you right home. If you shoots anything in the water, never mind how rough, you
can bet Three Eyes'll bring it. If you drops anything off the komatik, you can just send him back,
15 and he'll find it for you if 'tis a mile behind. I
takes him fishin' because if I lose a fish off t' hook,
Three Eyes'll go in after it, and mostly get him too.
'Deed, I wouldn't be here yarnin' to-night if it
wasn't for that great white brute there under the
20 table."

At this remark the dog's eyes looked up, though
his chin remained glued to the floor between his
great furry paws, and he seemed to smile as he
pretended to sleep again.

25 "Come New Year there was nothin' in the cupboard, and for tea us was drinkin' the spruce tops
and boilin' water. When March came in, flour

LINE **3.** **swiles:** seals. **14.** **komatik:** sled.

was scarce enough, too, and if us couldn't get
swiles it looked like starvation. February had gone
out blustersome, and there was nothin' but the
open water left. At last, however, the winds
shifted, and the ice began to run in. It was long
before dawnin' next day when me and Three Eyes
was out lookin' for swiles. The wind had pinned
the runnin' ice ag'in' the standin' edge, and it
looked good swilin' ice, too. I thought it was as
well to die one way as another, and so here goes
— and we started out across the floe.

"As luck would have it, there wasn't a sign
o' swiles near to, but Three Eyes was rangin' ahead
and searchin' everywhere. When he was about
three miles out he gave tongue, and soon I had a
dozen fine old fellows, and two or three white-coats
killed, close to the outer edge.

"I didn't like t' look o' things too well, for I felt
sure t' wind had veered by the feelin' in the air.
So I laced up one for Three Eyes, and started off
as hard as I could go, haulin' one myself. I knew
right then t' wind had really changed, for it were
right ahead again, and what's more I knew that
if it shifted the ice off even a few yards, us'd have
little chance of ever seein' home again. I reckon
that must have made me careless, for I had barely
time to see us was on black ice before in she goes,
and I was strugglin' in the water. I can't swim,
Doctor; t' water's too cold down here to learn, but

somehow I got hold of t' edge and hung on. But there was no gettin' out for me; t' heavy pans is far too high out o' water — and so I thought t' end had come, and I tell you I thought of the wife
5 and children. It so happened Three Eyes had better sense, and had gone round the young ice. He must have missed me right off, for though he was haulin' a heavy old dog harp, he was on the nearest pan starin' right at me when I got my
10 eyes clear o' water. As I minds it now, he must have done his thinkin' quick, knowin' I couldn't last many seconds in that water. For almost before I knew what had happened, he had heaved me the line that was fast to the swile, mind you,
15 and as soon as he felt me catch hold, he started to haul me out o' t' water. What he really done was to run round and round t' hole quite quicklike, and t' line, which was fast to t' old harp at t' other end, just had to come into my hands.

20 "I thinks still, Doctor, he thought it out hisself, for he isn't much of a dog for talk and show, as you knows, but that time he fairly let hisself go. Well, us was hurryin' all we knowed how before that happened, but now I had to cut the swile loose
25 and run for my life. My clothes was freezin' like boards, and even that little time lost might mean that we wouldn't be able to land. And land us

---

LINE **2.** **pans:** blocks of ice. **8.** **harp:** seal.

did only by God's mercy. For instead of the whole floe goin' straight off, it had wheeled round, and though there was open water all round when us reached t' edge, by runnin' along us just got a corner that touched t' shore ice as it wheeled, and so got home safe, glad enough, even though us had no swile, and only dry flour again that night for supper. Only Three Eyes seemed unhappy, somehow, though you may be sure he got all I had to give him to eat, but I guess he was wishin' he had had his supper before he left those swiles.

"Well, sir, t' next day, and t' next day, and t' day after that, Three Eyes and me was out from daylight till dark lookin' for them swiles, or any others that we could find. But no luck came along, and I was so sure that that ice had gone that I had given up hope altogether. So the next day I never went out at all. I never mistrusted either but that Three Eyes was home, too, that morning, till just about midday, when I called, but couldn't find a sign of him. No one had seen him goin' out, and if he left that day he must have started before daylight.

"Anyhow, when I went out on t' cliff to look for him, I saw him gallopin' home along t' edge, just as hard as he could come. Of course you may say that dogs can't talk, Doctor, but that's just the difference — Three Eyes can mostly make you understand what it is he wants. He soon

131

told me, anyhow, that he wanted me to come along. So I gets my gun right off, and away I goes after him, runnin' just all I could to keep up, too.

5   "There's a small island that's little better than a lot of cobbly rocks off t' south end o' t' main

He soon told me that he wanted me to come along.

island — lyin' out, I guess, some few hundred yards from the beach. That was all I could see besides ice when we got at last to t' land's end.
10 But Three Eyes didn't stop there — down he goes, jumps right in off t' edge, and swims off to t' rocks. Well, sir, when he came back, all I knew was that he had had his supper, and it had been swile meat, too.

15   "That's how he told me where those swiles had

gone. Next day me and all the boys hauled t'
punt down to t' edge, and went off in her. Sure
enough, there were our swiles. When that floe
wheeled, t' outer edge must have stuck right on the
point of the island, and then gone on, leavin' the 5
pans with our swiles jammed against the little
island. Anyhow, there was six old harps and four
whitecoats. I minds t' number as if it was yesterday; and that was meat enough for our crowd,
whatever else happened, to tide us till t' fish 10
struck in, or t' traders came back with summer
supplies.

"Lie down, there, Three Eyes," he added in the
same breath; and I noticed for the first time that
the dog had got up while he was finishing the story, 15
and was pressing his chin down on Jerry's knee
to attract his attention, while his bright eyes were
fixed motionlessly on Jerry's. They said, quite
intelligently, "That's all right, master. I only
wish I had the chance to do it all over again." 20

I noticed also that Jerry rubbed the dog's head
even while he pretended to scold him. And I
don't think tears were far from Jerry's eyes either.
But then, the logs were burning a little low, and he
wasn't looking my way. 25

BRUCE: A FIRE-DOG OF NEW YORK

Sarah Noble Ives

"You'll have to take him in, if I bide myself," said James MacMurray.

Engine Company No. — looked on with much interest as the captain addressed the unusual appli-
5 cant: a man six feet two in his red woolen socks, with a shock of red hair nearly as incendiary as the footwear, and with Scotland written all over him. By his side, watching the chief expectantly, stood the bonniest Highland collie that ever waved a
10 friendly tail. His glossy black coat was set off by a collar and waistcoat of tan, and he was as beautiful as his master was big and brawny.

"Mowbray didn't mention the dog when he spoke of you. But if the men don't object, I don't.
15 He looks like a good specimen."

"Ye'll not find a better. Bruce has been with me upwards of two year, and a finer herder you'll not find in New Jersey."

The chief laughed.

Reprinted from Sarah Noble Ives' *A Fire-Dog of New York* by permission of The Century Co.

134

"There won't be much herding to do in the fire department, unless you can teach him to herd the crowds, and keep 'em out from under our feet at a blaze; and he won't find them lambs to handle, either." ⁵

"It's a fine mascot he'll be making." Tim Callahan spoke from the depths of the room, where he was polishing the engine brasses.

"There's one of the men to speak for himself," said Captain Warner. "We'll make a try at ¹⁰ taking him on, and see how it goes. What did you say his name was?"

"Robert Bruce MacMurray, and it's a fit name. He's a king among collies."

"No doubt as to his nationality, at any rate," ¹⁵ laughed the captain.

So Bruce became a member of Engine Company No. —, and the stock farm in New Jersey where his master had trained him knew him no more. Instead of herding sheep and cattle, he had to ²⁰ learn to avoid teams in the rushing whirl of New York traffic. It was difficult, and at first he was dazed by the never-ending pell-mell of it; but he was young, and he soon forgot the quiet meadows and the lazy cattle, and learned to love the hurly- ²⁵ burly, the roar and rattle of wheels on the pavements, the shriek of the brakes on the Elevated, and the steady, tireless hum of the great hive. Following his master's example, he settled down into the daily routine of the station, as well as into the hearts of the fire-laddies.

They were a fine set of men, those big, strong chaps, with the courage of heroes to do and die in ₅times of danger, and the tenderness which grew out of their trade of life-saving. The captain looked upon his company with great pride, and he, as well as some of the others, had, tucked away with his treasures, medals for courage in action. ₁₀James MacMurray hugged himself for pleasure at the thought that fortune had thrown him among men of his own kind.

As for Bruce, his life in New Jersey had given him a love for horses; and who did not love these ₁₅magnificent specimens formerly found in New York's engine houses, now gone, alas! before the inrush of auto-trucks and engines? Bruce certainly divided his allegiance between the men and the four-footed heroes, and gave to the latter his ₂₀special attention. He saw to it three times a day that they were properly fed and watered, he superintended their rubbing down and grooming, and sanctioned, by a wag of his tail, the preparation of their beds at night.

₂₅ The rest of the work of the engine house was also performed under his eye of approval. The big brass engine could never have been kept in such a

LINE **18.** **allegiance:** devotion.

state of shining radiance without Bruce as over-lord. Tim Callahan laughed, as he swabbed on the polish and rubbed it down :

"Sure now, Bruce, and what'd you be doing to me if I forgot to shine one of those nuts? You'd 5 herd me back and make me do my work over again, I'll be bound. And as for Pete Tinkum there, he never in all his life bullied that floor to the extent he has since we had a mascot to our names, glory be! It was a grand day when you 10 dropped into our midst, James MacMurray, you son of a Scotch thistle."

So the ordinary doings of the day passed, with much rough, good-humored banter. Evenings the men sat around in a room on the upper floor 15 of the engine house, telling stories, reading, or playing cards. The room would have passed muster and taken a prize in any company of New England housewifely products, so spandy clean it was. The row of white iron bedsteads was a 20 joy to see, with their covers turned down, all at the same angle. On the floor, by the side of each one, stood a pair of rubber boots, with soles so thick that the wearer might slosh about freely in the neighborhood of the hydrant with no fear of 25 wet feet; also he might trample over broken glass and never risk a puncture. Fastened to the boots was a pair of heavy trousers, made so that a fire-man, waking to the alarm in the night, had only

to step into the whole "contraption" and pull the
fastening straps up over his shoulders. Coats and
helmets were hung on the engine and hose cart,
to be donned when under way, thus reducing to a
5 minimum the time for dressing.

At night Bruce slept at the foot of MacMurray's
bed, with one ear cocked for the fire alarm; and
when it rang, no matter what the day's weariness
might have been, Bruce was down the stair and at
10 his post before the quickest man among them
could slide down the pole, or the horses, released
automatically from their stalls, could leap to their
places. It was a sight worth seeing as he barked
and capered, apparently sure that the harness could
15 not have dropped to its place and been buckled
on by the first man down, had he not been there
to bark his orders. When the great doors swung
open and the engine leaped out, Bruce took his
place under it, or as near under as the shower of
20 sparks and coals would permit; and to the scene
of action he galloped as did the horses, as faithful
to the fiery monster as its own belching smoke.
He grew to have a real passion for a fire. Daytime or nighttime, it was always the same; where
25 the engine went, there went Bruce, certain that no
blaze could be quenched without him.

People of the neighborhood grew to look for the
black wraith that moved like the very shadow of
the engine. The hose cart he did not favor at all,

even when his master rode thereon. The sparks
that singed his coat never made him swerve from
his allegiance to the brass fire-devil. The small
boys watched him rapturously, and a night call
would find more than one pajama-clad worshiper 5
looking out of a window to see the "fire-dog."
Daytimes they lingered enviously around, as near
the engine as the rules allowed. But they could
adore only from a distance. The law of the engine
company forbade familiarity with small boys, and 10
Bruce was a keeper of the law. He might wave
his brush amiably if a particularly enticing whistle
attracted his attention, but never did his wooers
win him from the straight and narrow path. The
"fire-dog" remained as aloof and inspiring as the 15
big engine itself.

Now, there are fires and rumors of fires in New
York City, but with most of them the prompt
dash and the finely trained equipment bring the
danger to an end in its very beginnings. Occasion- 20
ally, however, a fire will work out of sight and does
not disclose itself until it has made good headway.
Then it means a stiff fight and no recess for all
hands, even to save adjoining buildings. Sometimes, too, a fire will start in highly combustible 25
material, and then look out ! The red demons leap
and clutch everything in sight, and even a hurry
call to every company within range fails to check
the flames.

This is what happened on a windy autumn night. A big paper factory on Eleventh Avenue caught fire in the basement, and the flames went racing and howling skyward, gutting floor after floor, till 5 the whole place was a seething flame. It was not a case of saving the building itself; that was doomed from the first up-flying spark; but of keeping the fire from spreading. Calls were sent in for all the available engines in the district.

10 It was a wild scene; the flames leaping and roaring; the streams of water going bravely into the red furnace, only to issue forth again in the clouds of steam and vapor; the network of rubber serpents, each manned at the nozzle by sweating, 15 helmeted heroes; the shouting and howling of the crowd, as floor after floor disappeared in the dragon's mouth; the yells of the firemen, as they popped out of neighboring skylights and proceeded to wet down the roofs that were dangerously near 20 — it was pandemonium.

And through it all the only quiet things were the horses. Quivering with excitement, they stood at their posts, waiting only the word of command that meant time for the drenched and weary men 25 to be taken home. The mad fury of the fire held every man, however, gritting his teeth over his special duty. In the turmoil, Pete Tinkum, who

---

LINE **20.** **pandemonium:** riotous uproar.

drove the engine that night for Company No. —,
Bruce's engine, did not see that the fire was beginning to blaze at the corner of the block where his
horses stood; no one noticed.

The heat grew fiercer and fiercer, and then the [5]
horse nearest the flame quietly and without a moan
dropped in his tracks. No one saw but Bruce,
who, as usual during a fire, remained in charge of
his engine. Surely it was wrong that a horse, one
of HIS horses, should die! [10]

Bruce darted toward a man who was toiling
along with a great flapping hose, and tried to
get his attention. He did not even look at the
dog.

He tried the chief, whom he knew; but the chief [15]
only said, "Back, Bruce; out of the way!" From
man to man he ran, vainly trying to get their
attention. Then out of a black doorway came Pete
Tinkum, waving an ax and looking wildly for a
spare man to help him on the roofs, where a new [20]
blaze was starting.

Pouf! He was nearly knocked flat by the rush
of the dog, who leaped upon him, barking and
pawing him frantically.

Pete stopped. This was unusual in Bruce, who [25]
had hitherto behaved himself so well when the
company was in action.

"For the love of Mike! What are ye up to?"
said Pete as he righted himself.

Bruce dropped to the ground, and turned toward his engine, then looked back at Pete and barked.

"What's wrong, I say?"

Then Pete looked and saw the fallen horse just in time to save the others, who were slowly suffocating. And after that roofs might burn for all of Pete, with his beloved horses dying at their post. He lost no time in getting them to a place of safety.

And there was mourning that night at Engine House No. — for a good horse fallen. And there was rejoicing, too, because of a dog, who had proved himself a fit companion of heroes.

At another fire, also, Bruce became a life-saver. A tenement on Twentieth Street packed with human beings caught fire, and for hours every nerve of every man in every company on the spot was strained almost to the breaking point. People hurled themselves from windows into nets; people climbed down gutter spouts, or dropped themselves hand over hand from cornice to blind, from blind to window sill, and so to safety — or death on the pavement below. One mother went mad for a moment, and refused to give up her baby to the fireman on the ladder. Whereupon mother and child were seized bodily, and carried shrieking to the ground.

It was a fire with more smoke than flame, and the halls and stairways were so choked with the black fumes that it took the most dogged courage of the pluckiest men to go in and find the beings huddled behind doors, or lying where they had fallen at the very window sills. The firemen could not stay long at the work; they were compelled to come out to save their own lives, leaving others to 5 go on with the task.

One more dash, and the last room would be searched, and every one still living would be out of the building; the fire, too, was getting under control, but the smoke was still dense and awful. 10 In the death-filled atmosphere James MacMurray and Cummings, with a no longer needed hose, groped their way along the hall of the second floor of the landing. In the general *mêlée* the railing had been broken, and MacMurray, not knowing 15 this, reached out to find it, overreached himself, stumbled, and fell head foremost into the hall below. As he fell he put out a hand, caught at the edge of the landing, and thus broke the fall, but at the same time swung himself in under the stair- 20 case, where he lay, stunned and alone, in the reek of smoke.

It could not have been for long, or he would have been quite smothered. Cummings, who was ahead, made his way to the blessed air, unaware of the 25 fact that his working mate had fallen. The worst was over. Captain Warner hastily counted his staff.

Line **14.** *mêlée:* confusion.

"Where's MacMurray?"

"He went in with me after that hose," said Cummings. "He was right behind. Didn't he come out?"

No one had seen him.

"In after him, boys. He won't be higher than the second floor."

"Lucky," said Cummings. "The other stairways are broken."

Up to the second landing groped two men, feeling with their feet all over the darkened hallways. Nobody there, nobody in the room, no one in the hall below. The men returned to their mates.

"Can't find him. We'll have to get the ladder for that third story."

"Hark!" Captain Warner lifted his hand.

A dog was barking inside the tenement. Now a black collie appeared at the door, gave an impatient yelp, and disappeared again.

"I'll warrant he's found the boy!" cried Callahan.

After the dog he dashed, and in a minute he reappeared bearing the unconscious body of MacMurray.

"Give him fresh air," said the captain, pushing back the crowd. "He needs it bad. He's not dead, though."

"Aye, I'm all right," said MacMurray, lifting

himself dizzily on his elbow. "How did you find me in the smoke?"

"Bruce found you. You were under the staircase, where no sane fireman would ever think of falling. How the dog smelled you in that smoke passes me."

"Well," said MacMurray, as he sat up and rubbed his bruises, "Bruce is a real canny dog. I dare be saying he'd find me in — in— "

"Mount Vesuvius," said Captain Warner, laughing.

"Aye," said James MacMurray solemnly, stumbling to his feet, "or in the bottomless pit."

For three January days, in the year of 189–, New York City had been lost in as wild a snowstorm as even the bravest dares to face. Side streets were blocked and almost impassable. Even Fifth Avenue, with the biggest effort of the street-cleaners, could boast only a bit of sidewalk and two narrow roadways, flanking a long-drawn-out Mont Blanc that stretched from Washington Square to Mount Morris Park. Then, on the fourth day, the dawn broke clear, breathing out of the north a wind with an icicle edge to it; a wind that bit into exposed faces and fingers until they cried out for mercy; a wind that pounced upon Harlem, and two minutes later was sweeping across the Battery and the bay. It sent the work of the cleaners whirling again in great unmanageable masses. It shrieked around the casements and ate into the hearts of the houses, until the janitors, even the stingiest, were fain to pile the coal high in the furnaces to save their own skins; and woe betide the unlucky who dwelt where furnaces were not!

And thereby hung a tale for the fire-fighters. Chimneys stuffed with soot and overheated; red-hot kitchen stoves, that set the chimney cupboards stewing until they sprang into flames; imperfect flues — the fireman can tell you the list of causes that force them out to fight harder than ever in the bitterest weather.

So it was now. All day the alarms kept ringing, and blaze after blaze was fought at odds with grim desperation. It was a hard day, and at nightfall, when the men on duty at Engine House No. — sat down to a supper brought in to them, that they might be on hand for a quick call, they did so with fervent prayers that they might be spared further labor, for they were spent.

It was snug and cozy in the little upper room that evening, despite the wild wind. But outside the gale was rising, and when Callahan reported that the mercury was "sitting in the bulb, begorra, with his hands and feet folded out of sight," every one shuddered and turned in for the night with extra blankets, and not even an ear left out for the alarm. Bruce got a blanket of his own, and

MacMurray was considered the lucky man to have such a hot-water bag to his feet. Sleep, well earned, settled down on all.

But it rang, oh yes! Hardly had the most case-hardened got his first forty winks when a call came, and a hurry call and a double call for all hands and the cook. The indicator told them that the fire was near Madison Avenue at ——'s big stables.

Clang! Clang! Clang! The horses bounded to their places, the harness leaped to their backs, and the men were booted, down the pole, and struggling into their coats along the running-board of the hose cart before you could mention John, the son of Robin.

"You'll have to bide at home to-night, Bruce," said MacMurray, as he swung to his place on the engine. "It's too cold a blast for them as has no need to go out."

Bruce's tail dropped to zero, and he stepped back a pace.

"Bide at home!" shouted MacMurray, as the doors flew open and the engine, spitting and belching and chugging, was drawn into the bleak, wind-swept snowdrifts. "Bide at home!" he yelled, as they turned a corner. Bruce stayed his feet until the rumble and clangor grew faint; then the ruling passion became too strong. A fire, and he not there to guard his engine? Impossible! Better would it be to disobey James MacMurray than to let his engine perish, and shame come upon Company No. — !

Down the street went a black collie, plunging and burrowing his way through the eddying drifts, now galloping faster where the street had been partly cleared. When the scene of the fire was reached, Bruce, a little breathless, but "still in the ring," was trotting at the tail of his own particular charge. MacMurray saw him, but this was no time for lessons in morals. The stables were burning fiercely, and there were thirty-five horses to be saved.

To the song of the north wind the fire added its crackle and roar. Already it had gained terrific headway; a dull red smoke poured from the blistered and broken windows; tongues of flame shot from the roof; the whole upper loft was one blazing mass; and the flying clouds above reflected the strange, unearthly light. Water was of no avail; it froze as it struck the building, and fell in great hissing icicles into the flames; the lower story was covered with a great casing of ice. In that awful cold the elements failed to destroy each other.

And underneath all this horror were thirty-five horses, whinnying, trembling, suffocating, and paralyzed with fear. Some of the firemen worked with the stable hands to get the horses out before the flooring should fall and engulf them. When those heavy beams gave way —! There was not a moment to be lost.

Hastily blinding the horses' eyes with blankets, the men led them, one by one, bucking and plunging, out into the street. Twelve they had saved and had returned for more when that unaccountable desire for the protection of their own roof seized the liberated beasts. There was a wild rush, the horses knocking down firemen and every obstacle. Panic seized those that were being led out and they broke away violently; in one moment all were back again under the roaring furnace of the loft.

A cry of anguish went up from the crowd that swayed and surged along the line of fighting police.

"Fire-mad!"

Yes, all of them! And now who would dare go in after them? Already the flames were licking between the boards above them, and the roof was tottering. When that fell the whole would go. Firemen dropped hose and axes and tried to force them back. No use. The smoke in the stables was so dense that nothing could be there long and breathe. James MacMurray battled desperately with a great cart horse, but it was blinded and insane from fright and absolutely unmanageable.

Something on four feet went galloping past MacMurray, after the horse he had vainly tried to save; something black, with a collar of tan and a waving tail. Now from the stables rang out a dog's bark, strong, clear, insistent.

"Bruce!" gasped MacMurray.

"Fire-mad, too, the little devil!" said Callahan, with a sob in his smoke-dried throat. "Head him off, you rascals!" he called to the quaking stable-hands. "He'll burn with the bunch!"

"Speak soft, man," said James MacMurray, grasping the Irishman by the shoulder, for Callahan was about to dive into the death trap. "Hold your wits and look! Look, man, don't you see the bonny laddie? He's herdin' them! He's herdin' the horses like sheep, and they dare not disobey. He's bitin' their heels now. Look how they mind him!"

"Glory be!" whispered Callahan, as if afraid of breaking the spell. "Will you see the likes of that! He's doing what no man would dare do!"

The crowd had stopped shouting; the roar of the wind and the flames went on, but every human heart stood still. Out they came — two — four — six — ten — TWENTY horses, dazed with the smoke, helpless with fear; but fear now of a thing that barked and bit their heels unceasingly, and would not let them rest. Lastly came a black collie, herding them carefully. No chance for one to turn back, they must go on, goaded relentlessly. Still the crowd kept silent.

"Has he got them all?"

"No, but he's saved twenty. Likely the others are suffocated with the smoke."

On they went; then, as the cold struck them, the horses looked back at their burning home and paused. Would they rush again? Yes! No! Robert Bruce MacMurray, with his stock-farm training, keen, quick, sharpened to the task, never gave them a loophole. Barking, biting, jumping on them, nipping at their heels, anywhere, but always between them and the danger, he forced them to belie their instincts and go on whither they were driven.

Then the crowd broke into such a cheer as drowned the voices of fire and storm. The horses at the sound surged backward, and then broke into a mad rush, helter-skelter. The mob leaped back to let them through — twenty horses and one black-and-tan collie — down the side street to Madison Avenue through the whirling drifts, away from the hell of smoke and flame and ruin.

Down the avenue they galloped until Bruce herded them into another side street, out of sight and sound of the fire. Twenty horses saved and one hero the more! Against the wall of a brewery he brought them together and held them, shivering in the icy tempest, until the stable hands captured them and led them to shelter in other stables.

Down on his knees went James MacMurray, he and the dog almost disappearing in the big

151

snowdrift, into which they rolled. The strong man caught the dog in his arms and called him his dear and his "Croodlin' doo"; and he picked him up and held him, kicking and struggling, high above his own unhelmeted red head, while the crowd laughed, cheered, cried, yelled, and forgot all about the other fire-lads, who were still struggling with the waning fire. There was just one thing for them, and that was a collie with a singed black-and-tan coat, whose name was Robert Bruce MacMurray.

The following week Engine-House No. — was astonished to see a smart and polished delivery wagon, driven by a smart and beliveried flunky, draw up impressively at their door. From the inside of the vehicle the flunky produced and delivered a package marked: "Robert Bruce MacMurray."

Callahan, with mouth agape, received it and looked at the address, wondering.

"Hey, MacMurray, I think your dog is receiving a wedding present. It's a grand time for the company when Tiffany drives up to its door."

MacMurray took the box. "It's very well gotten up," he said, turning it over and regarding its white and shining magnificence.

"Open it, man," said Cummings, as he and the others came up to look.

"It's a wonderful thing. Where do you think it came from?"

"Open it; open it! Here, I'll whip those ribbons off with a whack of my knife."

"No, no, Callahan, I'll untie it. 'Tis a bonny ₅ box, and I wouldn't clip the strings. Gently, now; 'tis of leather!"

"It's a proud day for the engine house, and for me."

There, in the soft radiance of its cushioned bed, lay a magnificent dog collar, just Bruce's size.

"And a plate of solid gold tacked to it, by the ₁₀ saints! Look, there's wording on it. Will you read it, now?" said Callahan, lifting it from its cushion and handing it to the captain, who had just come in.

The Magic Spear

The captain read aloud:

ROBERT BRUCE MACMURRAY
THE FIRE-DOG

In grateful remembrance of services rendered on the night of
5   January 27th, 189 —
From (owner of stables) to the dog who saved the lives of
twenty horses

Bruce looked up wonderingly as MacMurray slipped the circle over his head.

10 "It's a proud day for the engine house, and for me," said the man. His voice trembled on the last word.

"It's a proud day for the whole company, by the same token," said Callahan. "I was expecting
15 to see a crown out of that box. Long be the day before Bruce gathers with the saints and wears a HALO."

PUTNAM: A HORSE

R. H. Platt, Jr.

As we got nearer Pekin the mud walls of the villages turned to brick walls; and the road turned more and more into a street. Finally, it seemed like just one long continuous city with open fields beyond the houses on each side. 5

When the storming started my section was caught in a cut. The order was to get into action at all costs. We could hear the rattle of firing, with now and then the crash of one of the old Krupp guns that the Boxers were using. We knew it was 10 in earnest, but couldn't move the guns backward or forward, so jammed was the road. So Reilly came back and ordered us up the side of the cut! I suppose it was a forty-degree slope but it *looked* like a perpendicular cliff. "Are these horses like 15 flies that can go up the side of a wall, or ain't they?" was what crossed my mind. "Well, here's finding out!" I turned my team into the bank and gave the order to march.

Reprinted from R. H. Platt, Jr.'s *Mr. Archer U.S.A.* by permission of Doubleday, Page & Co.

The Magic Spear

The lead and the swing were digging in their toes and going up. Then old Putnam, the finest horse-flesh in the service, struck the cliff, and behind him started the gun, two tons of steel, with the ⁵limber filled. The gun hit the cliff suddenly, and just as suddenly there was a loud snap, and a yell from the driver on Putnam's back. The big horse heaved back a step; the forward trace toggle had snapped, and the whole team quit — except ¹⁰Putnam.

Then something happened that never happened before and will never happen again. It is the most historic horse story in the army. Soldiers have argued about it around the mess tables; ¹⁵officers have told it to recruits in driving classes. It has been forgotten only since 1918, but not by the Old-Timers.

It is this: Putnam heaved and swayed — then he took the bit in his teeth and started up the ²⁰bank, pulling not only the gun but the five other horses along with him. He didn't go right up — he fought every step — the handsomest fight you can imagine. His nostrils bulged out, his eyes opened wide, too; his muscles shook and knotted

---

LINE **1.** **lead:** leading pair of horses. **swing:** middle pair of the six-horse team. **5.** **limber:** detachable fore part of a gun carriage, bearing ammunition chests. **8.** **trace:** one of two side straps connecting the collar of a harness with the swingletree. **toggle:** a fastening.

156

till it seemed they would burst through his skin;
his feet hammered into the ground and the dirt
spurted out behind them in streams and clouds;
when his hoof struck a stone, sparks flew out.
The other horses reared and fought against him, 5
but little by little up the steep cliff moved
that snarling, plunging, objecting swarm of horses,
and the two-ton load behind, with Putnam in
the middle conducting operations. He brought
it to the top — fifteen feet above the road — 10
and there he stopped and everything stopped
with him. The whole column below looked
up and saw six horses tangled together standing beside their gun. One of them was big, and
stood there with his head up, to catch the air, 15
black against the sky, and looking like the king of
horses that he was. Then after the soldiers, who
had all stopped to look, began to realize what
Putnam had done, a cheer went up. They cheered
him and called to him by name, and then went 20
about the business of war with fight put into them
by a horse.

The whole thing had happened so unexpectedly
that no help had been given Putnam. But now
with all the men to help, and six horses to a gun, 25
it took a long time and much trouble to get the rest
of the battery up.

From the high ground which Putnam had
gained, we saw for the first time the walls and

pagodas of Pekin, and the mountains of Mongolia behind. Right in front was the Ha-Ta Gate at the southeast corner of the Tartar Wall. Above the gate was a huge tower like a fortress, bigger
5 than a hundred buildings below it. That gate was then occupied by the Boxers. Behind this gate, although I didn't know it then, were the legations. We placed a few shrapnels against the tower and along the foot of the wall, until
10 the command came to move forward rapidly and storm the gate. Then it was that the biggest battle of the Chinese expedition started.

There are some dumb animals that aren't so stupid as men; and there are other animals that
15 you can feel an affection for, just as you do for people. Remember Putnam in China, and how he pulled a gun up a bank by himself and so helped to capture the city of Pekin. There was a horse for you! He was afterward named "Pekin" in
20 honor of what he had done. When Pekin was brought back to the Philippine Islands, he was left there for the rest of his life. In 1907 Captain McCloskey of the Fourth Field Artillery, who had once been in the Fifth and who knew Pekin, wrote
25 the history of the horse:

LINE 1. **pagodas:** elaborately ornamented sacred towers, usually connected with temples. **8. legations:** official buildings occupied by foreign ministers. **shrapnels:** artillery shells which explode when they strike, scattering small balls.

Putnam: A Horse

Jolo, Jolo, P. I., October 13, 1907

I certify that one horse now in Battery "F," Fifth Field Artillery, named Putnam (and commonly called Pekin), was assigned to the Yale Light Battery of Niantic, Conn., in 1898; that on the muster out of the battery he was trans- 5 ferred to the Quartermaster at Fort Hamilton, N. Y., where in September, 1898, he was assigned to Reilly's Light Battery "F," Fifth Field Artillery; that he was brought to Manila in April and was in the fights around Imus Bacoor in October, 1899, through Colonel Schwan's expedition through Cavite 10 Province in October and November, 1899; was taken to China in July, 1900; was in the battle of Pei Tsang, Yang Tsun, and other engagements of the Allied Forces during the march to rescue the legations. (While drawing a gun into position on a light, steep elevation at 3200 yards from the 15 S. E. corner of the Tartar City of Pekin, the trace broke behind the swing horse in front of Putnam and he drew his side of the gun up the hill alone.)

He was brought back from China in May, 1901, and transferred to the Fifteenth Battery at Pasay, since which time I 20 have not seen him until in Battery "F," Fifth Field Artillery, at Ft. Wm. McKinley on August 3rd, 1907.

Manus McCloskey,
Captain Field Artillery.

This extraordinary history was sent up through 25 channels by Colonel Brown, who recommended that the horse be retired. It was the only case of its kind:

LINE **9.** **Imus Bacoor:** ē'mŭs bà-kōōr'. **10. Cavite:** kà-vē'tā. **12. Pei Tsang:** pā tsäng. **Yang Tsun:** yäng tsŏŏn. **20. Pasay:** pà-sä'. **22. Ft. Wm. McKinley:** about five miles from Manila.

The Magic Spear

Headquarters Fifth Field Artillery
Fort Wm. McKinley, Rizal, P. I.
June 17, 1908

Adjutant General,
5   Philippine Division,
      Manila, P. I.

(Through Military Channels)

Sir:

I have the honor to inclose herewith military history of
10 the horse "Putnam" of Battery "F," Fifth Field Artillery,
certified to by Captain McCloskey, Fourth Field Artillery.
The services of this horse have been very unusual and
important. The animal distinguished himself in battle at
the capture of Pekin, performing the work of three horses at
15 a critical moment when the guns of Light Battery "F,"
(Reilly's) Fifth Artillery, were coming into action.

The animal is now old and unable to perform his duty
properly. He is very large and handsome and is a great pet
in the battery. Under ordinary circumstances such a horse
20 should be condemned; but on account of his distinguished
services he should be retained in service as long as he lives,
very light work only being required of him. He is entitled
to more than this, however, and it is therefore requested that
authority be granted not only to continue "Putnam" in
25 service, in some Field Artillery Battery serving here in the
Philippines, but that he be allowed to turn out on all occasions of ceremony, in rear of his battery, led by one of our
men.

Very respectfully,
30   E. T. Brown,
       Colonel, Fifth Field Artillery,
                Commanding.

160

Putman: A Horse

There wasn't a man or an officer who hadn't heard of that horse, and no request for retirement ever went up faster or came back faster with every indorsement gladly given. The first indorsement was by Pershing: 5

Headquarters
Fort William McKinley, Rizal, P. I.
June 21, 1908

Respectfully forward to the Adjutant General, Department of Luzon. 10

The recommendations contained in this letter are entirely approved.

This horse deserves the consideration that should be shown faithful service, and has earned the right to live to the end of his natural life at the expense of the Government. 15

John J. Pershing,
Brigadier General, U. S. A.
Commanding.

After a few more indorsements, the story and the request for retirement got up to Washington and 20 there the Adjutant General, and the Quartermaster General, and the Assistant Quartermaster General, and the Deputy Quartermaster General, and the Chief Quartermaster, and the Secretary of War approved it. After that, forage was ordered for 25 him until such time as he should die. There was a horse that was a creator of morale and an ornament to the service! When he died, at the age of twenty, instead of being cremated, he was given a military burial on a hill just outside Fort McKinley, in the Islands.

A PIONEER GIRL

Anna Howard Shaw

OUR two greatest menaces were wild animals and Indians, but as the days passed the first of these lost the early terrors with which we had associated them. We grew indifferent to the sounds that had made our first night a horror to us all — there 5 was even a certain homeliness in them — while we regarded with accustomed, almost *blasé* eyes the various furred creatures of which we caught distant glimpses as they slunk through the forest. Their experience with other settlers had taught them 10 caution; it soon became clear that they were as eager to avoid us as we were to shun them, and by common consent we gave each other ample elbow-room. But the Indians were all around us, and every settler had a collection of hair-raising tales 15 to tell of them. It was generally agreed that they were dangerous only when they were drunk; but as they were drunk whenever they could get whisky, and as whisky was constantly given them in

---

Reprinted from Anna Howard Shaw's *The Story of a Pioneer* by permission of Harper & Brothers.

LINE 7. *blasé* (blà′zā′) : indifferent; wearied; bored.

exchange for pelts and game, there was a harrowing doubt in our minds whenever they approached us.

In my first encounter with them I was alone in the woods at sunset with my small brother Harry. We were hunting a cow James had bought, and our young eyes were peering eagerly among the trees, on the alert for any moving object. Suddenly, at a little distance, and coming directly toward us, we saw a party of Indians. There were five of them, all men, walking in single file, as noiselessly as ghosts, their moccasined feet causing not even a rustle among the dry leaves that carpeted the woods. All the horrible stories we had heard of Indian cruelty flashed into our minds, and for a moment we were dumb with terror. Then I remembered having been told that the one thing one must not do before them is to show fear. Harry was carrying a rope with which we had expected to lead home our reluctant cow, and I seized one end of it and whispered to him that we would "play horse," pretending he was driving me. We pranced toward the Indians on feet that felt like lead, and with eyes so glazed by terror that we could see nothing save a line of moving figures; but as we passed them they did not give to our little impersonation of care-free children even the tribute of a side glance. They were, we realized, headed straight for our home; and after a few moments we doubled on our tracks and, keeping

at a safe distance from them among the trees, ran
back to warn our mother that they were coming.

As it happened, James was away, and mother
had to meet her unwelcome guests supported only
by her young children. She at once prepared a
meal, however, and when they arrived she welcomed
them calmly and gave them the best she had.
After they had eaten they began to point at and
demand objects they fancied in the room — my
brother's pipe, some tobacco, a bowl, and such
trifles — and my mother, who was afraid to annoy
them by refusal, gave them what they asked. They
were quite sober, and though they left without
expressing any appreciation of her hospitality, they
made her a second visit a few months later, bringing
a large quantity of venison and a bag of cranberries
as a graceful return. These Indians were Ottawas;
and later we became very friendly with them and
their tribe, even to the degree of attending one of
their dances, which I shall describe later.

Our second encounter with Indians was a less
agreeable experience. There were seven "Mar-
quette warriors" in the next group of callers, and
they were all intoxicated. Moreover, they had
brought with them several jugs of bad whisky —
the raw and craze-provoking product supplied them
by the fur dealers — and it was clear that our cabin
was to be the scene of an orgy. Fortunately, my
brother James was at home on this occasion, and

as the evening grew old and the Indians, grouped together around the fire, became more and more irresponsible, he devised a plan for our safety. Our attic was finished and its sole entrance was 5 by a ladder through a trapdoor. At James's whispered command my sister Eleanor slipped up into the attic, and from the back window let down a rope, to which he tied all the weapons we had — his gun and several axes. These Eleanor 10 drew up and concealed in one of the bunks. My brother then directed that as quietly as possible, and at long intervals, one member of the family after another was to slip up the ladder and into the attic, going quite casually, that the Indians might 15 not realize what we were doing. Once there, with the ladder drawn up after us and the trapdoor closed, we would be reasonably safe, unless our guests decided to burn the cabin.

The evening seemed endless, and was certainly 20 nerve-racking. The Indians ate everything in the house, and from my seat in a dim corner I watched them while my sisters waited on them. I can still see the tableau they made in the firelit room and hear the unfamiliar accents of their speech 25 as they talked together. Occasionally one of them would pull a hair from his head, seize his scalping knife, and cut the hair with it — a most unpleasant sight! When either of my sisters approached them, some of the Indians would make gestures, as if capturing and scalping her. Through it all, however, the whisky held their close attention, and it was due to this that we succeeded in reaching the attic unobserved, James coming last of all and drawing the ladder after him. Mother and the children were 5 then put to bed; but through that interminable night James and Eleanor lay flat upon the floor, watching through the cracks between the boards the revels of the drunken Indians, which grew wilder with every hour that crawled toward sun- 10 rise. There was no knowing when they would miss us or how soon their mood might change. At any moment they might make an attack upon us or set fire to the cabin. By dawn, however, their whisky was all gone, and they were in so deep a 15 stupor that, one after the other, the seven fell from their chairs to the floor, where they sprawled unconscious. When they awoke they left quietly and without trouble of any kind. They seemed a strangely subdued and chastened band; probably 20 they were wretchedly ill after their debauch on the adulterated whisky the traders had given them.

That autumn the Ottawa tribe had a great corn celebration, to which we and the other settlers were invited. James and my older sisters attended it, 25 and I went with them, by my own urgent invitation. It seemed to me that as I was sharing the

---

Line **21.** **debauch:** carouse; excessive drinking.

work and the perils of our new environment, I
might as well share its joys; and I finally succeeded
in making my family see the logic of this position.
The central feature of the festivity was a huge
5 kettle, many feet in circumference, into which the
Indians dropped the most extraordinary variety
of food we had ever seen combined. Deer heads
went into it whole, as well as every kind of meat and
vegetable the members of the tribe could procure.
10 We all ate some of this agreeable mixture, and
later, with one another, and even with the Indians,
we danced gaily to the music of a tom-tom and a
drum. The affair was extremely interesting until
the whisky entered and did its unpleasant work.
15 When our hosts began to fall over in the dance and
slumber where they lay, and when the squaws
began to show the same ill effects of their refresh-
ments, we unostentatiously slipped away.

During the winter life offered us few diversions
20 and many hardships. Our creek froze over, and
the water problem became a serious one, which
we met with increasing difficulty as the temperature
steadily fell. We melted snow and ice, and existed
through the frozen months, but with an amount
25 of discomfort which made us unwilling to repeat
at least that special phase of our experience. In
the spring, therefore, I made a well. Long before

LINE **18.** **unostentatiously:** without being noticed.

this, James had gone, and Harry and I were now
the only outdoor members of our working force.
Harry was still too small to help with the well;
but a young man, who had formed the neighborly
habit of riding eighteen miles to call on us, gave
me much friendly aid. We located the well with
a switch, and when we had dug as far as we could
reach with our spades, my assistant descended into
the hole and threw the earth up to the edge, from
which I in turn removed it. As the well grew
deeper we made a half-way shelf, on which I stood,
he throwing the earth on the shelf, and I shoveling
it up from that point. Later, as he descended still
farther into the hole we were making, he shoveled
the earth into buckets and passed them up to me,
I passing them on to my sister, who was now
pressed into service. When the excavation was
deep enough we made the wall of slabs of wood,
roughly joined together. I recall that well with
calm content. It was not a thing of beauty, but
it was a thoroughly practical well, and it remained
the only one we had during the twelve years the
family occupied the cabin.

During our first year there was no school within
ten miles of us, but this lack failed to sadden Harry
or me. We had brought with us from Lawrence a
box of books, in which, in winter months, when our
outdoor work was restricted, we found much comfort. They were the only books in that part of

the country, and we read them until we knew them all by heart. Moreover, father sent us regularly the New York *Independent*, and with this admirable literature, after reading it, we papered our
5 walls. Thus, on stormy days, we could lie on the settle or the floor and read the *Independent* over again with increased interest and pleasure.

Occasionally father sent us the *Ledger*, but here mother drew a definite line. She had a special
10 dislike for that periodical, and her severest comment on any woman was that she was the type who would "keep a dog, make saleratus biscuit, and read the New York *Ledger* in the daytime." Our modest library also contained several histories of
15 Greece and Rome, which must have been good ones, for years later, when I entered college, I passed my examination in ancient history with no other preparation than this reading. There were also a few arithmetics and algebras, a historical novel or
20 two, and the inevitable copy of *Uncle Tom's Cabin*, whose pages I had freely moistened with my tears.

When the advantages of public education were finally extended to me, at thirteen, by the opening of a school three miles from our home, I accepted
25 them with growing reluctance. The teacher was a spinster forty-four years of age — and the only

---

LINE 6. **settle:** long bench with a high back. **12. saleratus:** cooking soda.

genuine "old maid" I have ever met who was not a married woman or a man. She was the real thing, and her name, Prudence Duncan, seemed the fitting label for her rigidly uncompromising personality. I graced Prudence's school for three 5 months, and then left it at her fervid request. I had walked six miles a day through trackless woods and western blizzards to get what she could give me, but she had little to offer my awakened and critical mind. My reading and my Lawrence 10 school work had already taught me more than Prudence knew — a fact we both inwardly admitted and fiercely resented from our different viewpoints. Beyond doubt I was a pert and trying young person. I lost no opportunity to lead Prudence beyond her 15 intellectual depth and leave her there, and Prudence vented her chagrin not alone upon me, but upon my little brother. I became a thorn in her side, and one day, after an especially unpleasant episode in which Harry also figured, she plucked me out, 20 as it were, and cast me for ever from her. From that time I studied at home, where I was a much more valuable economic factor than I had been in school.

LINE **4.** **uncompromising:** strict. **17.** **chagrin:** dismay.

CLARA BARTON

Rebecca Deming Moore

THE Barton family was made very happy on the Christmas of 1821 with the gift of a baby girl. The four older sisters and brothers gave the baby a royal welcome, though they little thought that
5 this gift was also to be a Christmas present to the whole world. This baby was Clara Barton, called in Civil War times the "Angel of the Battlefield," and known by all nations as the founder of the American Red Cross Society.

10 Baby Clara grew up to be the pet of the family, although no coddling was allowed on the Barton farm in Oxford, Massachusetts. Each member of the family wanted to teach her something, and Clara was equally eager to learn.

15 Mrs. Barton taught her daughter self-reliance. Nothing could have been worth more to the girl who was to be the first woman to carry organized aid to the wounded on an American battlefield. Mrs. Barton also taught Clara to sew, to cook, and
20 to be an excellent housekeeper.

Reprinted from *When They Were Girls* by Rebecca Deming Moore, published by F. A. Owen Publishing Company; copyrighted 1923.

Clara Barton

Clara was particularly grateful for this knowledge and had countless opportunities to use it. Once a dying soldier whispered his wish for a custard pie, crinkly around the edge, to remind him of home. With what materials she could get together, Miss Barton made the pie and scalloped the edge with her finger, just as her mother had taught her to do in the farm kitchen.

It was Big Brother David who taught the little sister many things that were to make her a very practical "Angel of the Battlefield." At five years of age, thanks to his training, she rode wild horses like a young Mexican. This skill in managing any horse meant the saving of countless lives when she had to gallop all night in a trooper's saddle to reach the wounded men. David taught her, also, to drive a nail straight, to tie a knot that would hold, and to think and act quickly.

From her father Clara heard thrilling tales of his fighting in the Revolutionary War under "Mad Anthony" Wayne. These stories doubtless made a deep impression on the youthful listener. Little did she realize that in the years to come she, too, would play an important part on many battlefields.

Clara Barton attended a boarding school for a short time. However, she received her education chiefly at home, being taught by her brother and then by a tutor. Later she had an opportunity for more advanced study at a near-by school.

The Magic Spear

The little farm girl was busy and happy from morning until night, for she loved to do things. She went for the cows, helped with the milking and churning, and had a hand in planting the potatoes. When the house was being painted, she begged to help with that, too, and she learned how to mix the paint as well as to put it on. Once she went into her brother's factory and learned how to weave cloth.

Her first experience as a nurse came at the age of eleven when Big Brother David was injured by a fall. For two years this cheerful, patient little nurse scarcely left his bedside.

When she was only fifteen years old, Clara Barton began to teach school. She taught well, too, for she understood girls and boys. It seemed as if she had found the work that she best liked to do. However, after eighteen years of teaching, her health necessitated her giving up this profession. Clara Barton did not know how to be idle; so she went to Washington and secured a position in the Patent Office.

When the Civil War broke out, many wounded soldiers were brought to Washington. Clara Barton helped to care for these boys, some of whom were her former pupils from Massachusetts. She also sent out appeals for money and supplies.

As Miss Barton saw the wounded taken from the transports, she was extremely sorry for them because they did not have proper care. She felt that she must go to nurse the soldiers who were close to the battlefields. This was entirely against army regulations, but Miss Barton was very persistent. She was finally allowed to take her store of bandages and other supplies to the front, where they were most needed. 5

People used to ask Miss Barton if she had not always been brave. The woman who walked coolly through Fredericksburg when every street was a firing line answered, telling of her childhood: "I was a shrinking little bundle of fears — fears of 10 thunder, fears of strange faces, fears of my strange self." It was when the shy girl forgot herself in working for others that she forgot her fears.

Bravery and willingness to help others, however, would have been of little use to Clara Barton had 15 she not been level-headed. The ability to see what should be done next and the ability to do it quickly and well were of equal value. It seemed as if Clara Barton worked magic, but her magic was only a mixture of common sense and a great pity for the 20 suffering.

Once at Antietam, when there seemed to be nothing to feed to the wounded men, she noticed that the medicine had been packed in fine meal. Quickly she borrowed several big kettles from the 25 farm where they were quartered, and she soon was serving the men with steaming gruel.

At another time, at nightfall, one of the doctors complained about the mismanagement that left him with a thousand wounded men to care for and only an inch of candle for a light. Miss Barton had fortunately brought along several boxes of lanterns, which she gave him. Her remarkable forethought meant the saving of many a life that night.

After the Civil War Clara Barton did not give up her work of mercy. For four years she helped to trace missing soldiers.

While in Europe, during the Franco-Prussian War, she saw the wonderful work that the Red Cross societies abroad were doing. She was deeply impressed with the value of such an organization and immediately decided that, upon her return to the United States, she would do all that she could to interest her country in the Red Cross.

Miss Barton worked for years to persuade the United States to found an American Red Cross Society. "We shall never have another war," people objected. However, Miss Barton pointed out that in time of great floods, fires, earthquakes, and other disasters lives could be saved by organized aid. At last she was successful, for in 1882 the American Red Cross Society came into being. Clara Barton was its president for many years.

The Red Cross banner was first unfurled for service in this country at Miss Barton's home at Dansville, New York, where she established a local chapter to aid the forest-fire sufferers in Michigan.

Clara Barton

Ever since that time the Red Cross has continued to give its efficient aid wherever needed. It had an exceptional opportunity during the World War to prove its worth. Our country has cause for deep gratitude to Clara Barton. 5

Clara Barton risked her life on sixteen battle-fields of the Civil War to care for the wounded. She founded the organization that has brought relief to thousands of people in war and disaster. She did great deeds, but they were possible only 10 because she had learned to do the little things of life well.

Friday

CAPTAIN SCOTT

James Matthew Barrie

ON the night of my original meeting with Scott, he was but lately home from his first adventure into the antarctic, and my chief recollection of the occasion is that, having found the entrancing man, 5 I was unable to leave him. In vain he escorted me through the streets of London to my home, for when he had said good night I then escorted him to his, and so it went on I know not for how long through the small hours. Our talk was 10 largely a comparison of the life of action (which he pooh-poohed) with the loathly life of those who sit at home (which I scorned); but I also remember that he assured me he was of Scotch extraction. As the subject never seems to have been resumed 15 between us, I afterwards wondered whether I had drawn this from him with a promise that, if his reply was satisfactory, I would let him go to bed. However, the family traditions (they are nothing more) do bring him from across the border. Ac-20 cording to them his great-great-grandfather was the Scott of Brownhead whose estates were sequestered after the '45. His dwelling was razed to the ground and he fled with his wife, to whom after some grim privations a son was born in a fisherman's hut on September 14, 1745. This son eventually settled in Devon, where he prospered, for it was in the beautiful house of Oatlands that he died. He had four sons, all in the Royal Navy, of whom the eldest had as youngest child John Edward Scott, father of the Captain Scott who was born at Oatlands on June 6, 1868. About the same date, or perhaps a little earlier, it was decided that the boy should go into the navy like so many of his forbears.

I have been asked to write a few pages about those early days of Scott at Oatlands, so that the boys who read this book may have some slight acquaintance with the boy who became Captain Scott; and they may be relieved to learn (as it holds out some chance for themselves) that the man who did so many heroic things does not make his first appearance as a hero. He enters history aged six, blue-eyed, long-haired, inexpressibly slight and in velveteen, being held out at arm's length by a servant and dripping horribly, like a half-drowned kitten. This is the earliest recollection of him of a sister, who was too young to join in a

---

LINE **2.** **sequestered:** confiscated.

children's party on that fatal day. But Con, as he
was always called, had intimated to her that from a
window she would be able to see him taking a noble
lead in the festivities of the garden, and she looked;
5 and that is what she saw. He had been showing
his guests how superbly he could jump the leat,
and had fallen into it.

Leat is a Devonshire term for a running stream,
and a branch of the leat ran through the Oatlands
10 garden while there was another branch, more
venturesome, at the bottom of the fields. These
were the waters first plowed by Scott, and he
invented many ways of being in them accidentally,
it being forbidden to enter them of intent. Thus
15 he taught his sisters and a brother a new version of
the oldest probably of all pastimes, the game of
"Touch." You had to touch "across the leat,"
and, with a little good fortune, one of you went in.
Once you were wet, it did not so much matter
20 though you got wetter.

An easy way of getting to the leat at the foot of
the fields was to walk there, but by the time he was
eight Scott scorned the easy ways. He invented
parents who sternly forbade all approach to this
25 dangerous waterway; he turned them into enemies
of his country and of himself (he was now an
admiral), and led parties of gallant tars to the
stream by ways hitherto unthought of. At the foot
of the avenue was an oak tree which hung over the

road, and thus by dropping from this tree you got into open country. The tree was (at this time) of an enormous size, with sufficient room to conceal a navy, and the navy consisted mainly of the sisters and the young brother. All had to be ready at any 5 moment to leap from the tree and join issue with the enemy on the leat. In the fields there was also a mighty ocean, called by dull grown-ups "the pond," and here Scott's battleship lay moored. It seems for some time to have been an English vessel, but by 10 and by he was impelled, as all boys are, to blow something up, and he could think of nothing more splendid for his purpose than the battleship. Thus did it become promptly a ship of the enemy doing serious damage to the trade of those parts, and the 15 valiant Con took to walking about with lips pursed, brows frowning as he cogitated how to remove the Terror of Devon. You may picture the sisters and brother trotting by his side and looking anxiously into his set face. At last he decided to blow the 20 accursed thing up with gunpowder. His crew cheered, and then waited to be sent to the local shop for a pennyworth of gunpowder. But Con made his own gunpowder, none of the faithful were ever told how, and on a great day the train was 25 laid. Con applied the match and ordered all to stand back. A deafening explosion was expected,

---

LINE **17.** **cogitated:** meditated; thought.

but a mere puff of flame was all that came; the Terror of Devon, which to the unimaginative was only a painted plank, still rode the waters. With many boys this would be the end of the story, but not with Con. He again retired to the making of gunpowder, and did not desist from his endeavors until he had blown that plank sky-high.

His first knife is a great event in the life of a boy; it is probably the first memory of many of them, and they are nearly always given it on condition that they keep it shut. So it was with Con, and a few minutes after he had sworn that he would not open it he was begging for permission to use it on a tempting sapling. "Very well," his father said grimly, "but remember, if you hurt yourself, don't expect any sympathy from me." The knife was opened, and to cut himself rather badly proved as easy as falling into the leat. The father, however, had not noticed, and the boy put his bleeding hand into his pocket and walked on unconcernedly. He was really considerably damaged; and this is a good story of a child of seven who all his life suffered extreme nausea from the sight of blood; even in the *Discovery* days, to get accustomed to "seeing red," he had to force himself to watch Dr. Wilson skinning his specimens.

When he was about eight Con passed out of the hands of a governess, and became a schoolboy, first at a day school in Stoke Damerel and later

at Stubbington House, Fareham. He rode grandly
between Oatlands and Stoke Damerel on his pony,
Beppo, which bucked in vain when he was on it,
but had an ingratiating way of depositing other
riders on the road. From what one knows of him 5
later this is a characteristic story. One day he
dismounted to look over a gate at a view which
impressed him (not very boyish this), and when
he recovered from a brown study there was no
Beppo to be seen. He walked the seven miles 10
home, but what was characteristic was that he
called at police stations on the way to give practical
details of his loss and a description of the pony.
Few children would have thought of this, but Scott
was naturally a strange mixture of the dreamy and 15
the practical, and never more practical than immediately after he had been dreamy. He forgot
place and time altogether when thus abstracted. I
remember the first time he dined with me, when a
number of well-known men had come to meet him, 20
he arrived some two hours late. He had dressed
to come out, then fallen into one of his reveries,
forgotten all about the engagement, dined by himself and gone early to bed. Just as he was falling
asleep he remembered where he should be, arose 25
hastily, and joined us as speedily as possible. It was
equally characteristic of him to say of the other

Line **4. ingratiating:** winning confidence.

guests that it was pleasant to a sailor to meet so many interesting people. When I said that to them the sailor was by far the most interesting person in the room, he shouted with mirth. It always 5 amused Scott to find that any one thought him a person of importance.

I suppose every one takes for granted that in his childhood, as later when he made his great marches, Scott was muscular and strongly built. This was 10 so far from being the case that there were many anxious consultations over him, and the local doctor said he could not become a sailor as he could never hope to obtain the necessary number of inches around the chest. He was delicate and inclined 15 to be pigeon-breasted. Judging from a portrait of him, in his first uniform as a naval cadet, all this had gone by the time he was thirteen, but unfortunately there are no letters of this period extant; and thus little can be said of his years on the 20 *Britannia*, where "you never felt hot in your bunk because you could always twist, and sleep with your feet out at a porthole." He became a cadet captain, a post none can reach who is not thought well of by the other boys as well as by their 25 instructors, but none of them foresaw that he was likely to become anybody in particular. He was still "Old Mooney," as his father had dubbed him,

LINE **15.** **pigeon-breasted:** narrow-chested with breastbone pressed forward and outward.

because of his dreamy mind; it was an effort to him
to work hard, he cast a wistful eye on "slackers,"
he was not a good loser, he was untidy to the point
of slovenliness, and he had a fierce temper. All
this I think has been proved to me up to the hilt, 5
and as I am very sure that the boy of fifteen or so
cannot be very different from the man he grows
into, it leaves me puzzled. The Scott I knew, or
thought I knew, was physically as hard as nails and
flung himself into work or play with a vehemence 10
I cannot remember ever to have seen equaled.
I have fished with him, played cricket and football
with him and other games, those of his own inven-
tion being of a particularly arduous kind, for they
always had a moment when the other players were 15
privileged to fling a hard ball at your undefended
head. "Slackness" was the last quality you would
think of when you saw him bearing down on you
with that ball, and it was the last he asked of you if
you were bearing down on him. He was equally 20
strenuous of work; indeed I have no clearer recollection of him than his way of running from play to
work or work to play, so that there should be the
least possible time between. It is the "time between" that is the "slacker's" kingdom, and Scott 25
lived less in it than any one I can recall. Again, I
found him the best of losers, with a shout of delight

Line **10.** vehemence: force; earnestness.

for every good stroke by an opponent: what is called an ideal sportsman. He was very neat and correct in his dress, quite a model for the youth who come after him, but that we take as a matter
5 of course; it is "good form" in the navy. His temper I should have said was bullet-proof. I have never seen him begin to lose it for a second of time, and I have seen him in circumstances where the loss of it would have been excusable.

10 However, "the boy makes the man," and Scott was none of those things I saw in him but something better. The faults of his youth must have lived on in him as in all of us, but he got to know they were there and he took an iron grip of them and never
15 let go his hold. It was this self-control more than anything else that made the man of him of whom we have all become so proud. I get many proofs of this in correspondence dealing with his manhood days. The horror of slackness was turned into a
20 very passion for keeping himself "fit." Thus we find him at one time taking charge of a dog, a "Big Dane," so that he could race it all the way between work and home, a distance of three miles. Even when he was getting the *Discovery* ready and doing
25 daily the work of several men, he might have been seen running through the streets of London from Savile Row or the Admiralty to his home, not

---

LINE **27.** **Savile Row:** street in London. **Admiralty:** offices of the British Naval Board.

because there was no time for other methods of
progression, but because he must be fit, fit, fit.
No more "Old Mooney" for him; he kept an eye
for ever on that gentleman, and became doggedly
the most practical of men. And practical in the [5]
cheeriest of ways. In 1894 a disastrous change
came over the fortunes of the family, the father's
money being lost, and then Scott was practical
indeed. A letter he wrote at this time to his mother,
tenderly taking everything and everybody on his [10]
shoulders, must be one of the best letters ever
written by a son, and I hope it may be some day
published. His mother was the great person of
his early life, more to him even than his brother
or his father, whom circumstances had deprived [15]
of the glory of following the sailor's profession
and whose ambitions were all bound up in this
son, determined that Con should do the big things
he had not done himself. For the rest of his
life Con became the head of the family, devoting [20]
his time and his means to them, not in an it-must-
be-done manner, but with joy and even gaiety.
He never seems to have shown a gayer front
then when the troubles fell, and at a farm to
which they retired for a time he became famous [25]
as a provider of concerts. Not only must there
be no "Old Mooney" in him, but it must be driven
out of every one. His concerts, in which he took
a leading part, became celebrated in the district,

deputations called to beg for another, and once in these words, "Wull 'ee gie we a concert over our way when the comic young gentleman be here along?"

5 Some servants having had to go at this period, Scott conceived the idea that he must even help domestically in the house, and took his own bedroom under his charge with results that were satisfactory to the casual eye, though not to the eyes of his 10 sisters. It was about this time that he slew the demon of untidiness so far as his own dress was concerned and doggedly became a model for still younger officers. Not that his dress was fine. While there were others to help he would not spend 15 his small means on himself, and he would arrive home in frayed garments that he had grown out of and in very tarnished lace. But neat as a pin. In the days when he returned from his first voyage in the antarctic and all England was talking of him, 20 one of his most novel adventures was at last to go to a first-class tailor and be provided with a first-class suit. He was as elated by the possession of this as a child. When going about the country lecturing in those days he traveled third class, 25 though he was sometimes met at the station by mayors and corporations and red carpets.

The hot tempers of his youth must still have lain

LINE **1.** **deputations:** persons acting for others. **9. casual:** chance. **26. corporations:** town governments; aldermen.

hidden, but by now the control was complete.
Even in the naval cadet days of which unfortunately
there is so little to tell, his old friends who remember the tempers remember also the sunny smile
that dissipated them. When I knew him the sunny 5
smile was there frequently, and was indeed his
greatest personal adornment, but the tempers never
reached the surface. He had become master of his
fate and captain of his soul.

In 1886 Scott became a middy on the *Boadicea*, 10
and later on various ships, one of them the *Rover*,
of which Admiral Fisher was at that time commander. The admiral has a recollection of a little
black pig having been found under his bunk one
night. He cannot swear that Scott was the leading 15
culprit, but Scott was certainly one of several who
had to finish the night on deck as a punishment.
In 1888 Scott passed his examinations for sub-
lieutenant, with four first-class honors and one
second, and so left his boyhood behind. I cannot 20
refrain, however, from adding as a conclusion to
these notes a letter from Sir Courtauld Thomson
that gives a very attractive glimpse of him in this
same year:

"In the late winter a quarter of a century ago I 25
had to find my way from San Francisco to Alaska.
The railway was snowed up and the only transport

LINE **10.** *Boadicea:* a ship named after a British queen.

available at the moment was an ill-found tramp
steamer. My fellow passengers were mostly Cali-
fornians hurrying off to a new mining camp and,
with the crew, looked a very unpleasant lot of ruf-
5 fians. Three singularly unprepossessing Frisco
toughs joined me in my cabin, which was none too
large for a single person. I was then told that yet
another had somehow to be wedged in. While I
was wondering if he could be a more ill-favored or
10 dirtier specimen of humanity than the others the
last comer suddenly appeared — the jolliest and
breeziest English naval second lieutenant. It was
Con Scott. I had never seen him before, but we at
once became friends and remained so till the end.
15 He was going up to join his ship, which, I think,
was the *Amphion*, at Esquimault, B. C.

"As soon as we got outside the Golden Gates we
ran into a full gale which lasted all the way to
Victoria, B. C.   The ship was so overcrowded that a
20 large number of women and children were allowed
to sleep on the floor of the only saloon there was on
condition that they got up early, so that the rest of
the passengers could come in for breakfast and the
other meals.

25   "I need scarcely say that owing to the heavy
weather hardly a woman was able to get up,
and the saloon was soon in an indescribable
condition. Practically no attempt was made to
serve meals, and the few so-called stewards were

themselves mostly out of action from drink or seasickness.

"Nearly all the male passengers who were able to be about spent their time drinking and quarreling. The deck cargo and some of our top hamper were 5 washed away, and the cabins got their share of the waves that were washing the deck.

"Then it was I first knew that Con Scott was no ordinary human being. Though at that time still only a boy he practically took command of the 10 passengers and was at once accepted by them as their boss during the rest of the trip. With a small body of volunteers he led an attack on the saloon — dressed the mothers, washed the children, fed the babies, swabbed down the floors and nursed the 15 sick, and performed every imaginable service for all hands. On deck he settled the quarrels and established order either by his personality, or, if necessary, by his fists. Practically by day and night he worked for the common good, never sparing himself, 20 and with his infectious smile gradually made us all feel the whole thing was jolly good fun.

"I dare say there are still some of the passengers like myself who, after a quarter of a century, have imprinted on their minds the vision of this fair- 25 haired English sailor boy with the laughing blue eyes who at that early age knew how to sacrifice himself for the welfare and happiness of others."

THE LAST LETTERS

of

Captain Scott

[Captain Scott spent his last days in writing letters and diaries, from which the following selections are taken.]

To Mrs. E. A. Wilson

My dear Mrs. Wilson,

If this letter reaches you Bill and I will have gone out together.   We are very near it now and I should
5 like you to know how splendid he was at the end —
everlastingly cheerful and ready to sacrifice himself
for others, never a word of blame to me for leading
him into this mess.   He is not suffering, luckily,
at least only minor discomforts.

10   His eyes have a comfortable blue look of hope,
and his mind is peaceful with the satisfaction of his
faith in regarding himself as part of the great scheme
of the Almighty.   I can do no more to comfort you
than to tell you that he died as he lived, a brave,
15 true man — the best of comrades and stanchest of
friends.

My whole heart goes out to you in pity.

Yours,

R. Scott

The Last Letters of Captain Scott

To Mrs. Bowers

My dear Mrs. Bowers,

I am afraid this will reach you after one of the heaviest blows of your life.

I write when we are very near the end of our journey, and I am finishing it in company with two gallant, noble gentlemen.   One of these is your son. He had come to be one of my closest and soundest friends, and I appreciate his wonderful upright nature, his ability, and energy. As the troubles have thickened, his dauntless spirit ever shone brighter and he has remained cheerful, hopeful, and indomitable to the end.

The ways of Providence are inscrutable, but there must be some reason why such a young, vigorous, and promising life is taken.

My whole heart goes out in pity for you.

Yours,
R. Scott

To the end he has talked of you and his sisters. One sees what a happy home he must have had, and perhaps it is well to look back on nothing but happiness.

He remains unselfish, self-reliant, and splendidly hopeful to the end, believing in God's mercy to you.

193

The Magic Spear

My dear Barrie,

We are pegging out in a very comfortless spot.
Hoping this letter may be found and sent to you, I
5 write a word of farewell. . . . More practically I
want you to help my widow and my boy — your
godson. We are showing that Englishmen can
still die with a bold spirit, fighting it out to the end.
It will be known that we have accomplished our
10 object in reaching the Pole, and that we have done
everything possible, even to sacrificing ourselves
in order to save sick companions. I think this
makes an example for Englishmen of the future, and
that the country ought to help those who are left
15 behind to mourn us. I leave my poor girl and your
godson, Wilson leaves a widow, and Edgar Evans
also a widow in humble circumstances. Do what
you can to get their claims recognized. Good-by.
I am not at all afraid of the end, but sad to miss
20 many a humble pleasure which I had planned for
the future on our long marches. I may not have
proved a great explorer, but we have done the
greatest march ever made and come very near to
great success. Good-by, my dear friend.

25
                                        Yours ever,
                                          R. Scott

We are in a desperate state, feet frozen, etc. No
fuel and a long way from food, but it would do your

194

heart good to be in our tent, to hear our songs and the cheery conversation as to what we will do when we get to Hut Point.

Later. — We are very near the end, but have not and will not lose our good cheer. We have four days of storm in our tent and nowhere's food or fuel. We did intend to finish ourselves when things proved like this, but we have decided to die naturally in the track.

As a dying man, my dear friend, be good to my wife and child. Give the boy a chance in life if the State won't do it. He ought to have good stuff in him. . . . I never met a man in my life whom I admired and loved more than you, but I never could show you how much your friendship meant to me, for you had much to give and I nothing.

To Sir Edgar Speyer

Dated, March 16, 1912, Lat. 79.5

My dear Sir Edgar,

I hope this may reach you. I fear we must go and that it leaves the Expedition in a bad muddle. But we have been to the Pole and we shall die like gentlemen. I regret only for the women we leave behind.

I thank you a thousand times for your help and support and your generous kindness. If this diary is found it will show how we stuck by dying companions and fought the thing out well to the end. I think this will show that the spirit of pluck and the power to endure have not passed out of our race. . . .

Wilson, the best fellow that ever stepped, has sacrificed himself again and again to the sick men of the party. . . .

I write to many friends hoping the letters will reach them some time after we are found next year.

We very nearly came through, and it's a pity to have missed it, but lately I have felt that we have overshot our mark. No one is to blame and I hope no attempt will be made to suggest that we have lacked support.

Good-by to you and your dear kind wife.

Yours ever sincerely,

R. Scott

To Sir Francis Charles Bridgeman

My dear Sir Francis,

I fear we have slipped up; a close shave; I am writing a few letters which I hope will be delivered some day. I want to thank you for the friendship you gave me of late years, and to tell you how extraordinarily pleasant I found it to serve under you. I want to tell you that I was *not* too old for this job. It was the younger men that went under first. . . . After all we are setting a good example to our countrymen, if not by getting into a tight place, by

facing it like men when we were there.   We could
have come through had we neglected the sick.

Good-by, and good-by to dear Lady Bridgeman.

Yours ever,

R. Scott   5

Excuse writing — it is —40°, and has been for
nigh a month.

Your friend,

R. Scott

The Great God has called me and I feel it will 10
add a fearful blow to the heavy ones that have
fallen on you in life.   But take comfort in that I
die at peace with the world and myself — not
afraid.

Indeed it has been most singularly unfortunate, 15
for the risks I have taken never seemed excessive.

I want to tell you that we have missed getting
through by a narrow margin which was justifiably
within the risk of such a journey. . . .   After all,
we have given our lives for our country — we have 20
actually made the longest journey on record, and we
have been the first Englishmen at the south pole.

You must understand that it is too cold to write
much.

It's a pity the luck doesn't come our way, because 25
every detail of equipment is right.

I shall not have suffered any pain, but leave the
world fresh from harness and full of good health

197

and vigor. This is decided already — when provisions come to an end we simply stop unless we are within easy distance of another depot. Therefore you must not imagine a great tragedy. We are very anxious of course, and have been for weeks, but our splendid physical condition and our appetites compensate for all discomfort.

Since writing the above we got to within eleven miles of our depot, with one hot meal and two days' cold food. We should have got through but have been held for four days by a frightful storm. I think the best chance has gone. We have decided not to kill ourselves, but to fight to the last for that depot, but in the fighting there is a painless end. So don't worry. The inevitable must be faced. You urged me to be leader of this party, and I know you felt it would be dangerous.

Make the boy interested in natural history if you can; it is better than games; they encourage it at some schools. I know you will keep him in the open air.

Above all, he must guard and you must guard him against indolence. Make him a strenuous man. I had to force myself into being strenuous, as you know — had always an inclination to be idle.

There is a piece of the Union Jack I put up at the south pole in my private kit bag, together with Amundsen's black flag and other trifles. Send a small piece of the Union Jack to the King and a small piece to Queen Alexandra.

What lots and lots I could tell you of this journey. How much better has it been than lounging in too great comfort at home. What tales you would have for the boy. But what a price to pay.

Tell Sir Clements, I thought much of him and never regretted his putting me in command of the *Discovery*.

MESSAGE TO THE PUBLIC

The causes of the disaster are not due to faulty organization, but to misfortune in all risks which had to be undertaken.

1. The loss of pony transport in March, 1911, obliged me to start later than I had intended, and obliged the limits of stuff transported to be narrowed.

2. The weather throughout the outward journey, and especially the long gale in 83° S., stopped us.

3. The soft snow in lower reaches of glacier again reduced pace.

We fought these untoward events with a will and conquered, but it cut into our provision reserve.

Every detail of our food supplies, clothing, and depots made on the interior ice-sheet and over that long stretch of 700 miles to the Pole and back worked out to perfection. The advance party would have returned to the glacier in fine form and with surplus of food, but for the astonishing failure of

the man whom we had least expected to fail.   Edgar
Evans was thought the strongest man of the party.

The Beardmore Glacier is not difficult in fine
weather, but on our return we did not get a single
5 completely fine day; this with a sick companion
enormously increased our anxieties.

As I have said elsewhere we got into frightfully
rough ice and Edgar Evans received a concussion of
the brain — he died a natural death, but left us a
10 shaken party with the season unduly advanced.

But all the facts above enumerated were as nothing to the surprise which awaited us on the Barrier.
I maintain that our arrangements for returning
were quite adequate, and that no one in the world
15 would have expected the temperatures and surfaces
which we encountered at this time of the year.
On the summit in lat. $85°$, $86°$ we had $-20°$, $-30°$.
On the Barrier in lat. $82°$, 10,000 feet lower, we had
$-30°$ in the day, $-47°$ at night pretty regularly,
20 with continuous head wind during our day marches.
It is clear that these circumstances come on very
suddenly, and our wreck is certainly due to this
sudden advent of severe weather, which does not
seem to have any satisfactory cause.   I do not
25 think human beings ever came through such a
month as we have come through and we should have
got through in spite of the weather but for the
sickening of a second companion, Captain Oates,
and a shortage of fuel in our depots for which I

cannot account, and finally, but for the storm which has fallen on us within eleven miles of the depot at which we hoped to secure our final supplies. Surely misfortune could scarcely have exceeded this last blow. We arrived within eleven miles of our old One Ton Camp with fuel for one last meal and food for two days. For four days we have been unable to leave the tent — the gale howling about us. We are weak, writing is difficult, but for my own sake I do not regret this journey, which has shown that Englishmen can endure hardships, help one another, and meet death with as great a fortitude as ever in the past. We took risks, we knew we took them; things have come out against us, and therefore we have no cause for complaint, but bow to the will of Providence, determined still to do our best to the last. But if we have been willing to give our lives to this enterprise, which is for the honor of our country, I appeal to our countrymen to see that those who depend on us are properly cared for.

Had we lived, I should have had a tale to tell of hardihood, endurance, and courage of my companions which would have stirred the heart of every Englishman. These rough notes and our dead bodies must tell the tale, but surely, surely, a great rich country like ours will see that those who are dependent on us are properly provided for.

R. Scott

WILLIAM CRAWFORD GORGAS

Marie D. Gorgas
and
Burton J. Hendrick

GORGAS began his work at Havana in March, 1901; the deaths subsequent to this were precisely five, and these took place in July and August of that year. In 1905, it is true, there was another out-
5 break, but it was promptly checked by the Gorgas methods. Since then eighteen years have passed, and not a single case of the disease has been reported in the city that for centuries had been its main headquarters. Dramatic as yellow fever has always
10 been, there is nothing in its history so dramatic as its sudden cessation. It was like a sea that had been tossed with storms for a century and a half and then, seemingly without warning, became as quiet as a mill pond. No wonder the whole
15 scientific world was awed in the presence of this tremendous fact. It signified that the human mind

Reprinted, by permission of Doubleday, Page & Co., from *William Crawford Gorgas : His Life and Work* by Marie D. Gorgas and Burton J. Hendrick.

LINE **2.** **subsequent to:** following. **11.** **cessation:** stop.

William Crawford Gorgas

had once more risen superior to Nature and had penetrated one of the secrets which she had cleverly hidden for ages. To Gorgas especially the real solemnity of the achievement was especially impressive. To him the thing meant more than 5 merely ridding a community of its most persistent scourge; it really opened a new outlook for man. From this date his life took on a new meaning — a definite meaning. What had been done in Cuba could be done in other disease-ridden countries; 10 what had been accomplished with yellow fever could be accomplished with similar plagues. At that time mighty areas of the earth's surface were inaccessible to man, chiefly because of contagious disease. Gorgas had demonstrated that 15 this was not inevitable. The belief that men could not live prosperously and happily in the tropics was now shown to be a myth. The redemption of such territories, the abolition of the diseases that had barred them to civilization, now became 20 Gorgas's life work. He was forty-eight years old, and, in prospect, he had added as much space to the earth's surface as Columbus himself.

Yet Gorgas never made any such claim as this. The destruction of mosquitoes was to occupy the 25 rest of his life, but he never withheld the chief glory from the man to whom, he believed, it was due.

LINE 7. scourge: plague. 14. inaccessible: beyond reach. 18. redemption: saving.

The Magic Spear

From now on the guiding influence of his life was Walter Reed. The two men kept closely in touch with each other during the performance in Havana. Each at first had certain doubts to remove. Gorgas, 5 when he began, was not certain that the mosquito was the only infective agent but his own success quickly demolished these doubts. Reed did not believe that yellow fever could be abolished by killing mosquitoes and their larvæ; but his skep-
10 ticism also was just as rapidly removed. The letters that passed between the two men at this time display the confidence and enthusiasm they entertained for each other. "The news from Havana is simply delightful," writes Reed on
15 July 29th. . . . "It shows that your acquaintance with the local conditions was much better than mine. That you have succeeded in throttling the epidemic appears beyond question and it is to your everlasting credit. A man of less discretion,
20 enthusiasm, and energy would have made a fiasco of it. Whereas you, my dear Gorgas, availing yourself of the results of the work at Camp Lazear, have rid that pesthole, Havana, of her yellow plague. All honor to you, my dear boy!"
25 "Really, my dear doctor," Reed wrote Gorgas in another letter, "when I think of the absence of yellow fever from Havana for a period of fifty days,

---

Line **9.** **skepticism:** unbelief.   **20.** **fiasco:** failure.

William Crawford Gorgas

I begin to feel like rejoicing that I was ever born!"
And Gorgas was just as generous to Reed. "Certainly," he wrote Reed on August 26, 1901, "the
work of proving the mosquito to be the transmitter
of yellow fever is as important a piece of work as [5]
has been done since Jenner's time, and, as far as the
United States is concerned, probably of more
importance; and yours was the guiding hand in the
whole matter. . . . I am very happy to serve in
the more humble rôle of being the first to put your [10]
discovery to extensive practical application."

Reed lived just long enough to witness the fruits
and the possibilities of his great discovery; his
labors in Havana had so weakened his frame that he
died, from an operation for appendicitis, in 1902, in [15]
his fifty-first year. He had no sincerer mourner
than Gorgas, who, for the rest of his life, never
missed an opportunity to witness his debt to Reed.
One day General M. Weaver was walking down
Connecticut Avenue, Washington, with his little [20]
granddaughter. He met Gorgas, then at the height
of his fame.

"Persis," said the general to the little girl, "this
is General Gorgas, one of our great men."

"No, my child," said Gorgas, in his soft accents, [25]
"not a great man; merely one who is trying to follow
in the footsteps of a great man — Walter Reed."

LINE **6.** **Jenner:** discoverer of vaccination. **10. rôle:** part.

The Magic Spear

Doctor Gorgas on his return from South Africa, in 1920, died in London, after a lingering illness. The London *Lancet*, probably the world's greatest medical journal, gave the great sanitarian this fine
5 tribute:

"The story of the riddance of Havana from the curse of yellow fever has been told often enough but deserves to be recalled here; for it was typical of Gorgas's work. During the last forty-five years
10 of Spanish rule on the island of Cuba the number of deaths from yellow fever occurring annually in the capital, although varying greatly from year to year, was never below 50, and many times exceeded 1,000. The work of Major Walter Reed and his
15 colleagues pointed strongly to the prevention of yellow fever being bound up with the destruction of the mosquito Culex (now called Stegomyia fasciata), or the prevention of its bites. Major Gorgas, as he then was, lost no time in putting this theory to a
20 practical trial. As he himself tersely phrased it, 'The only infected material from the towns looked after was the sick man, who was carefully sought out and screened from mosquitoes.' Havana was, and remained, in unrestricted communication with
25 half-a-dozen infected towns; commerce was not

LINE **4. sanitarian:** one interested in public health. **15. colleagues:** associates. **17. Stegomyia fasciata:** the mosquito which carries the cause of yellow fever. **20. tersely:** briefly.

interfered with and no restraint was placed upon the admission of clothing or bedding from infected localities; but under a purely antimosquito régime, during the year 1901–1902 only five deaths from yellow fever were recorded. Seldom has a scientific discovery been applied so promptly and successfully to an administrative problem.

"The reputation of Gorgas as a scientist has been challenged in certain quarters, in view of the fact that he was not responsible for the actual discoveries without which his work could not have been done. For this he needs no defense. Science and art are at their greatest when they join hands, and the man who acts as a link between discovery and its application needs a combination of qualities as rare as those of the pure investigator. It has been too much the pride of the seeker after abstract truth in the exact sciences to care little as to its application. But even when research has been undertaken with the sole aim of finding the cause of an endemic fever or the source of an infection, the successful investigator would often cut a poor figure as the organizer of an expedition to stamp out the scourge in the light of his discoveries. It is not only as a scientist but as a leader of men, as a hero of at least two of the most successful campaigns ever waged, that the name of Gorgas will always be gratefully

---

LINE **3.** **régime:** administration; system of ruling. **20. endemic:** peculiar to some country or people.

remembered. The formal procession with the body from Millbank under military escort to St. Paul's, and the ensuing ceremony in the Metropolitan Cathedral, are evidences of the reverence due
5 to a great benefactor of humanity which in this case are amply called for."

The funeral, at the special desire of the British government, took place in St. Paul's Cathedral. The American ambassador, Mr. John W. Davis,
10 and Mrs. Davis attended, and the King, Queen Alexandra, and the Duke of Connaught sent representatives. A description, printed in a British periodical, eloquently gives the spirit of the occasion and forms a fitting end to this narrative :

15 "A riderless horse walked up Ludgate Hill the other day behind its sleeping master, and if a horse can feel and know what happens, its heart must have been breaking — unless there came to it new strength in the pride it felt in the sight of its master
20 sleeping under the Stars and Stripes on his way to St. Paul's.

"For what was happening that day up Ludgate Hill was a rare and stirring thing. I looked down from the windows of the little House with Green
25 Shutters in the very shadow of the dome, and I thought that here indeed was a public opinion of which our London, and our country, and all the

---

LINE **15.** **Ludgate Hill:** a street in London.

entire world, might well be proud. For here was
no great Englishman, no great Briton, going to
his rest; here was a ragged, barefoot boy of Baltimore being carried to St. Paul's after his life's work
was done.   5

"He had done for the world one of the greatest
things that an American brain has ever done; he
made the Panama Canal after thousands of people
had died in the attempt.

"Now think how he began his life.   This is what 10
he told us:

"'I first came to Baltimore a ragged, barefoot
little rebel, with empty pockets and empty stomach.
My father had gone south with Lee's army.   At the
fall and destruction of Richmond my mother's 15
house with all that she had was burned, leaving her
stranded with six small children.   She came to
Baltimore and was cared for by friends.   These
memories are vivid with me, and can never be
effaced.'   20

"All these came up Ludgate Hill, and as the sun
poured down on this ancient way, our hearts and
ears throbbing with the solemn music of the Dead
March, we knew that we were looking on the passing of a man whose name would shine for ages in 25
the history of our race.

"It seemed good that death should find him here,
for so there came our opportunity to do a great man
honor.   He passed through the great door through

which the sun streams into the nave of St. Paul's, and there he lay with Nelson and Wellington and all that mighty host who came this way and passed into the universe.

5 "They will take him to his own land, but in truth he belongs to us all. He was one of life's great helpers, for he cleaned up foul places and made them sweet, and now, as they said of Lincoln, ' he belongs to the ages.'"

10 This funeral of a British major-general, in St. Paul's Cathedral, was the highest honor that Britain could pay a distinguished American. Its beauty and its solemnity will never be forgotten by those who witnessed it. But Gorgas's own country also 15 gave him its greatest honors. The body lay in state for four days in Washington, and, at the services in the Church of the Epiphany, all branches of the government and most foreign countries were represented.

20 The general was buried on one of the most beautiful slopes of Arlington — certainly an appropriate resting place for a man whose thoughts and activities, from his earliest days, had been associated with the American army.

LINE **21.** **Arlington:** national cemetery in Virginia, formerly the home of Robert E. Lee.

MARY WHITE

William Allen White

THE Associated Press reports carrying the news
of Mary White's death declared that it came as the
result of a fall from a horse.   How she would have
hooted at that !   She never fell from a horse in her
life.   Horses have fallen on her and with her — 5
"I'm always trying to hold 'em in my lap," she used
to say.   But she was proud of few things, and one
was that she could ride anything that had four
legs and hair.   Her death resulted not from a fall,
but from a blow on the head which fractured her 10
skull, and the blow came from the limb of an overhanging tree on the parking.

The last hour of her life was typical of its happiness.   She came home from a day's work at
school, topped off by a hard grind with the copy on 15
the High School Annual, and felt that a ride would
refresh her.   She climbed into her khakis, chatter-
ing to her mother about the work she was doing,
and hurried to get her horse and be out on the dirt
roads for the country air and the radiant green 20

Reprinted by permission of William Allen White.

fields of the spring. As she rode through the town on an easy gallop she kept waving at passers-by. She knew every one in town. For a decade the little figure with the long pigtail and the red hair ribbon 5 had been familiar on the streets of Emporia, and she got in the way of speaking to those who nodded at her. She passed the Kerrs, walking the horse, in front of the Normal Library, and waved at them; passed another friend a few hundred feet further 10 on, and waved at her. The horse was walking and as she turned into North Merchant Street she took off her cowboy hat, and the horse swung into a lope. She passed the Tripletts and waved her cowboy hat at them, still moving gaily north on Mer-15 chant Street. A *Gazette* carrier passed — a High School boy friend — and she waved at him, but with her bridle hand; the horse veered quickly, plunged into the parking where the low-hanging limb faced her, and, while she still looked back waving, the 20 blow came. But she did not fall from the horse; she slipped off, dazed a bit, staggered, and fell in a faint. She never quite recovered consciousness.

But she did not fall from the horse; neither was she riding fast. A year or so ago she used to go 25 like the wind. But that habit was broken, and she used the horse to get into the open to get fresh, hard exercise, and to work off a certain surplus energy that welled up in her and needed a physical outlet. That need had been in her heart for years.

Mary White

It was back of the impulse that kept the dauntless,
little brown-clad figure on the streets and country
roads of this community and built into a strong,
muscular body what had been a frail and sickly
frame during the first years of her life. But the 5
riding gave her more than a body. It released a
gay and hardy soul. She was the happiest thing
in the world. And she was happy because she was
enlarging her horizon. She came to know all sorts
and conditions of men; Charley O'Brien, the traffic 10
cop, was one of her best friends. W. L. Holtz,
the Latin teacher, was another. Tom O'Connor,
farmer-politican, and Rev. J. H. J. Rice, preacher
and police judge, and Frank Beach, music master,
were her special friends, and all the girls, black and 15
white, above the track and below the track, in
Pepville and Stringtown, were among her acquaint-
ances. And she brought home riotous stories of her
adventures. She loved to rollick; persiflage was
her natural expression at home. Her humor was a 20
continual bubble of joy. She seemed to think in
hyperbole and metaphor. She was mischievous
without malice, as full of faults as an old shoe. No
angel was Mary White, but an easy girl to live with,
for she never nursed a grouch five minutes in her life. 25

With all her eagerness for the out-of-doors, she
loved books. On her table when she left her room

LINE **19. persiflage:** flippant talk. **22. hyperbole:** ex-
aggeration.

were a book by Conrad, one by Galsworthy, *Creative Chemistry* by E. E. Slosson, and a Kipling book. She read Mark Twain, Dickens, and Kipling before she was ten — all of their writings. Wells and 5 Arnold Bennett particularly amused and diverted her. She was entered as a student in Wellesley in 1922; was assistant editor of the High School Annual this year, and in line for election to the editorship of the Annual next year. She was a 10 member of the executive committee of the High School Y. W. C. A.

Within the last two years she had begun to be moved by an ambition to draw. She began as most children do by scribbling in her school books, funny 15 pictures. She bought cartoon magazines and took a course — rather casually, naturally, for she was, after all, a child, with no strong purposes — and this year she tasted the first fruits of success by having her pictures accepted by the High School Annual. 20 But the thrill of delight she got when Mr. Ecord, of the Normal Annual, asked her to do the cartooning for that book this spring was too beautiful for words. She fell to her work with all her enthusiastic heart. Her drawings were accepted, and 25 her pride — always repressed by a lively sense of the ridiculousness of the figure she was cutting — was a really gorgeous thing to see. No successful artist ever drank a deeper draft of satisfaction than she took from the little fame her work was getting

among her schoolfellows. In her glory, she almost
forgot her horse — but never her car.

For she used the car as a jitney bus. It was her
social life. She never had a "party" in all her
nearly seventeen years — wouldn't have one; but 5
she never drove a block in the car in her life that she
didn't begin to fill the car with pick-ups! Everybody rode with Mary White — white and black,
old and young, rich and poor, men and women.
She liked nothing better than to fill the car full of 10
long-legged High School boys and an occasional girl,
and parade the town. She never had a "date,"
nor went to a dance, except once with her brother,
Bill, and the "boy proposition" didn't interest her
— yet. But young people — great, spring-break- 15
ing, varnish-cracking, fender-bending, door-sagging
carloads of "kids" — gave her great pleasure. Her
zests were keen. But the most fun she ever had in
her life was acting as chairman of the committee
that got up the big turkey dinner for the poor folks 20
at the county home; scores of pies, gallons of slaw;
jam, cakes, preserves, oranges, and a wilderness of
turkey were loaded in the car and taken to the
county home. And, being of a practical turn of
mind, she risked her own Christmas dinner by stay- 25
ing to see that the poor folks actually got it all.
Not that she was a cynic; she just disliked to tempt

LINE **21.** **slaw:** shredded raw cabbage.

215

folks. While there she found a blind colored uncle, very old, who could do nothing but make rag rugs, and she rustled up from her school friends rags enough to keep him busy for a season. The last
5 engagement she tried to make was to take the guests at the county home out for a car ride. And the last endeavor of her life was to try to get a rest room for colored girls in the High School. The poor she had always with her, and was glad of it.
10 She hungered and thirsted for righteousness; and was the most impious creature in the world. She joined the Congregational Church without consulting her parents; not particularly for her soul's good. She never had a thrill of piety in her life, and
15 would have hooted at a "testimony." But even as a little child she felt the church was an agency for helping people to more of life's abundance, and she wanted to help. She never wanted help for herself. Clothes meant little to her. It was a
20 fight to get a new rig on her; but eventually a harder fight to get it off. She never wore a jewel and had no ring but her High School class ring, and never asked for anything but a wrist watch. She refused to have her hair up; though she was nearly
25 seventeen. "Mother," she protested, "you don't know how much I get by with, in my braided pigtails, that I could not, with my hair up." Above every other passion of her life was her passion not to grow up, to be a child. The tomboy in her, which

Mary White

was big, seemed to loath to be put away forever in
skirts. She was a Peter Pan, who refused to grow up.

The services yesterday at the Congregational
Church were as she would have wished them; no
singing, no flowers save the big bunch of red roses 5
from her Brother Bill's Harvard classmen — Heavens, how proud that would have made her! and
the red roses from the *Gazette* force — in vases at her
head and feet. A short prayer, Paul's beautiful
essay on "Love" from the Thirteenth Chapter of 10
First Corinthians, some remarks about her demo-
cratic spirit by her friend, John H. J. Rice, pastor
and police judge, which she would have deprecated
if she could, a prayer sent down for her by her
friend, Carl Nau, and opening the service the slow, 15
poignant movement from Beethoven's Moonlight
Sonata, which she loved, and closing the service
a cutting from the joyously melancholy first movement of Tschaikowsky's *Pathetic Symphony*, which
she liked to hear in certain moods on the phono- 20
graph; then the Lord's Prayer by her friends in
the High School.

That was all.

For her pallbearers only her friends were chosen;
her Latin teacher — W. L. Holtz; her High School 25

Line **2.** **Peter Pan:** a delightful character in a play by
Sir James M. Barrie. Peter was a boy who never grew up.
13. deprecated: expressed disapproval of. **16. poignant:**
sharp; intense. **19. Tschaikowsky:** a great Russian composer.

principal, Rice Brown; her doctor, Frank Foncan-
non; her friend, W. W. Finney; her pal at the
Gazette office, Walter Hughes; and her brother
Bill. It would have made her smile to know that
5 her friend, Charley O'Brien the traffic cop, had been
transferred from Sixth and Commercial to the
corner near the church to direct her friends who
came to bid her good-by.

A rift in the clouds in a gray day threw a shaft of
10 sunlight upon her coffin as her nervous, energetic
little body sank to its last sleep. But the soul of
her, the glowing, gorgeous, fervent soul of her,
surely was flaming in eager joy upon some other
dawn.

MY CHILDHOOD

Michael Pupin

MY teacher in the village school never succeeded in making upon my mind that profound impression which was made upon it by the men at the neighborhood gatherings. They were men who had gone out into the world and taken an active part in the struggles of the world. Reading, writing, and arithmetic appeared to me like instruments of torture which the teacher, who, in my opinion at that time, knew nothing of the world, had invented in order to interfere as much as possible with my freedom, particularly when I had an important engagement with my chums and playmates.

But my mother soon convinced me that I was wrong. She could neither read nor write, and she told me that she always felt that she was blind, in spite of the clear vision of her eyes. So blind, indeed, that, as she expressed it, she did not dare venture into the world much beyond the confines of my native village. This was as far as I remember now the mode of reasoning which she would address to me: "My boy, if you wish to go out into the world

about which you hear so much at the neighborhood
gatherings, you must provide yourself with another
pair of eyes; the eyes of reading and writing.
There is so much wonderful knowledge and learning
5 in the world which you cannot get unless you can
read and write. Knowledge is the golden ladder
over which we climb to heaven; knowledge is the
light which illuminates our path through this life
and leads to a future life of everlasting glory." She
10 was a very pious woman, and had a rare knowledge
of both the Old and the New Testaments. The
Psalms were her favorite recitations. She knew
also the lives of saints. St. Sava was her favorite
saint. She was the first to make me understand
15 the story of the life of this wonderful Serb. This,
briefly stated, was the story which she told me:
Sava was the youngest son of the Serb Zhupan
Nemanya. At an early age he renounced his royal
titles and retired to a monastery on Mount Athos
20 and devoted many years to study and meditation.
He then returned to his native land, in the beginning of the thirteenth century, and became the first
Serbian archbishop and founded an autonomous
Serbian church. He also organized public schools
25 in his father's realm, where Serbian boys and girls
had an opportunity to learn how to read and write.
Thus he opened the eyes of the Serbian people,

LINE **17. Zhupan Nemanya:** zōō'pȧn nē-män'yȧ. **23. autonomous:** independent.

and the people in grateful recognition of these great services called him St. Sava the Educator, and praised forever his saintly name and memory. Seven hundred years had passed since St. Sava's time, but not one of them had passed without a memorial celebration dedicated to him in every town and in every home where a Serb lived.

This was a revelation to me. Like every schoolboy, I attended, of course, every year in January, the celebrations of St. Sava's day. On these occasions we unruly boys made fun of the big boy who in a trembling and awkward voice was reciting something about St. Sava, which the teacher had written out for him. After this recitation, the teacher, with a funny nasal twang, would do his best to supplement in a badly articulated speech what he had written out for the big boy, and finally the drowsy-looking priest would wind up with a sermon bristling with archaic Slavonic church expressions, which to us unruly boys sounded like awkward attempts of a Slovak mouse-trap dealer to speak Serbian. Our giggling merriment then reached a climax, and so, many mischievous chums never gave me a chance to catch the real meaning of the ceremonies on St. Sava's day. My mother's story of St. Sava and the way in which she told it made the image of St. Sava appear before me for the

LINE **19. archaic:** very old. **Slavonic:** relating to the Slavs, a European race.

221

first time in the light of a saint who glorified the value of books and of the art of writing.

I understood then why mother placed such value upon reading and writing. I vowed to devote myself to both, even if that should make it necessary to neglect my chums and playmates, and soon I convinced my mother that in reading and writing I could do at least as well as any boy. The teacher observed the change; he was astonished, and actually believed that a miracle had occurred. My mother believed in miracles, and told the teacher that the spirit of St. Sava was guiding me. One day she told him in my presence that in a dream she saw St. Sava lay his hands upon my head, and then turning to her say: "Daughter Piada, your boy will soon outgrow the village school of Idvor. Let him then go out into the world, where he can find more brain food for his hungry head." Next year the teacher selected me to make the recitation on St. Sava's day, and he wrote out the speech for me. My mother amended and amplified it and made me rehearse it for her over and over again. On St. Sava's day the first public speech of my life was delivered by me. The success was overwhelming. My chums, the unruly boys, did not giggle; on the contrary they looked interested, and that encouraged me much. The people said to one another that even old Baba Batikin could not have done much better. My mother cried for joy; my teacher shook his head, and the priest looked puzzled, and they both admitted that I had outgrown the village school of Idvor.

During those school days in Pančevo I passed my summer vacation in my native village. Idvor, just like the rest of Banat, lives principally from agriculture, and during harvest time it is as busy as a beehive. Old and young, man and beast, concentrate all their efforts upon the harvest operations. But nobody is busier than the Serbian ox. He is the most loyal and effective servant of the Serb peasant everywhere, and particularly in Banat. He does all the plowing in the spring, and he hauls the seasoned grain from the distant fertile fields to the threshing grounds in the village when the harvesting season is on. The commencement of the threshing operations marks the end of the strenuous efforts of the good old ox; his summer vacation begins, and he is sent to pasture lands to feed and to rest and to prepare himself for autumn hauling of the yellow corn and for the autumn plowing of the fields. The village boys who are not big enough to render much help on the threshing grounds are assigned to the task of watching over the grazing oxen during their summer vacation. The school vacation of the boys coincided with the vacation of the good old ox. Several summers I passed in that interesting occupation. These were my only summer schools,

and they were the most interesting schools that I
ever attended.

The oxen of the village were divided into herds
of about fifty head, and each herd was guarded by
a squad of some twelve boys from families owning
the oxen in the herd. Each squad was under the
command of a young man who was an experienced
herdsman. To watch a herd of fifty oxen was not
an easy task. In daytime the job was easy, because
the heat of the summer sun and the torments of the
ever-busy fly made the oxen hug the shade of the
trees, where they rested awaiting the cooler hours
of the day. At night, however, the task was
much more difficult. Being forced to hug the shade
of the trees during daytime, the oxen would get
but little enjoyment of the pasture, and so when
the night arrived they were quite hungry and
eagerly searched for the best of feed.

I must mention now that the pasture lands of
my native village lay alongside of territory of a
score of square miles which in some years were
all planted in corn. During the months of August
and September these vast cornfields were like deep
forests. Not far from Idvor and to the east of
the cornfields was a Rumanian settlement which
was notorious for its cattle thieves. The trick of
these thieves was to hide in the cornfields at night
and to wait until some cattle strayed into these
fields, when they would drive them away and hide

them somewhere in their own cornfields on the other side of their own village. To prevent the herd from straying into the cornfields at night was a great task, for the performance of which the boys had to be trained in daytime by their experienced leader. It goes without saying that each day we boys first worked off our superfluous energy in wrestling, swimming, hockey, and other strenuous games, and then settled down to the training of the arts of herdsman which we had to practice at night. One of these arts was signaling through the ground. Each boy had a knife with a long wooden handle. This knife was stuck deep into the ground. A sound was made by striking against the wooden handle, and the boys, lying down and pressing their ears close to the ground, had to estimate the direction and the distance of the origin of sound. Practice made us quite expert in this form of signaling. We knew at that time that the sound traveled through the ground far better than through the air, and that a hard and solid ground transmitted sound much better than the plowed-up ground. We knew, therefore, that the sound produced this way near the edge of the pasture land could not be heard in the soft ground of the cornfields stretching along the edge. A Rumanian cattle thief, hidden at night in the cornfields, could not hear our ground signals and could not locate us. Kos, the Slovenian, my teacher and interpreter of physical phenomena, could not explain this, and I doubt very much whether the average physicist of Europe at that time could have explained it. It is the basis of a discovery ₅ which I made about twenty-five years after my novel experiences in that herdsmen's summer school in Idvor.

On perfectly clear and quiescent summer nights on the plains of my native Banat, the stars are ₁₀ intensely bright and the sky looks black by contrast. "Thy hair is as black as the sky of a summer midnight" is a favorite saying of a Serbian lover to his ladylove. On such nights we could not see our grazing oxen when they were more than a few ₁₅ score of feet from us, but we could hear them if we pressed our ears close to the ground and listened. On such nights we boys had our work cut out for us. We were placed along a definite line at distances of some twenty yards apart. This was the ₂₀ dead-line, which separated the pasture lands from the cornfield territory. The motto of the French at Verdun was: "They shall not pass!" This was our motto, too, and it referred equally to out friends, the oxen, and to our enemies, the Rumanian ₂₅ cattle thieves. Our knife blades were deep in the ground and our ears were pressed against the handles. We could hear every step of the roaming

---

LINE **8.** **quiescent:** quiet.

oxen and even their grazing operations when they were sufficiently near to the dead-line. We knew that these grazing operations were regulated by the time of the night, and this we estimated by the position of certain constellations like Orion and the Pleiades. The positions of the evening star and of the morning star also were closely observed. Venus was our white star and Mars was called the red star. The Dipper, the North Star, and the Milky Way were our compass. We knew also that, when in the dead of the night we could hear the faint sound of the church bell of the Rumanian settlement about four miles to the east of us, then there was a breeze from the cornfields to the pasture lands, and that it carried the sweet perfume of the young corn to the hungry oxen, inviting them to the rich banquet table of the cornfields. On such nights our vigilance was redoubled. We were then all eyes and ears. Our ears were closely pressed to the ground and our eyes were riveted upon the stars above.

The light of the stars, the sound of the grazing oxen, and the faint strokes of the distant church bell were messages of caution which on those dark summer nights guided our vigilance over the precious herd. These messages appealed to us like the loving words of a friendly power, without

LINE **5.** **Orion:** ô-rī′ŏn. **6.** **Pleiades:** plē′yȧ-dēz.

The Magic Spear

whose aid we were helpless. They were the only signs of the world's existence which dominated our consciousness as, enveloped in the darkness of night and surrounded by countless burning stars, we
5 guarded the safety of our oxen. The rest of the world had gone out of existence; it began to reappear in our consciousness when the early dawn announced what we boys felt to be the divine command, "Let there be light," and the sun, heralded
10 by long white streamers, began to approach the eastern sky, and the earth gradually appeared as if by an act of creation. Every one of those mornings of fifty years ago appeared to us herdsmen to be witnessing the creation of the world — a world at
15 first of friendly sound and light messages which made us boys feel that a divine power was protecting us and our herd, and then a real terrestrial world, when the rising sun had separated the hostile mysteries of night from the friendly realities of the day.

20 Sound and light became thus associated in my early modes of thought with the divine method of speech and communication, and this belief was strengthened by my mother, who quoted the words of St. John: "In the beginning was the word, and
25 the word was with God, and the word was God."

I believed also that David, some of whose psalms, under the instruction of my mother, I knew by heart, and who in his youth was a shepherd, expressed my thoughts in his nineteenth psalm :

228

My Childhood

The Heavens declare the glory of God. . . .
        .   .   .   .

There is no speech nor language, where their voice is not
    heard.

Then, there is no Serb boy who has not heard
that beautiful Russian song by Lermontov, the *5*
great Russian poet, which says:

> Lonely I wander over the country road,
> And in the darkness the stony path is glimmering;
> Night is silent and the plains are whispering
> To God, and star speaketh to star.   *10*

Lermontov was a son of the Russian plains. He
saw the same burning stars in the blackness of a
summer midnight sky which I saw. He felt the
same thrill which David felt and through his psalms
transmitted to me during those watchful nights of *15*
fifty years ago. I pity the city-bred boy who has
never felt the mysterious force of that heavenly
thrill.

Sound and light being associated in my young
mind of fifty years ago with divine operations by *20*
means of which man communicates with man, beast
with beast, stars with stars, and man with his
Creator, it is obvious that I meditated much about
the nature of sound and of light. I still believe
that these modes of communication are the funda- *25*
mental operations in the physical universe and I
am still meditating about their nature.

LINE **5.** **Lermontov:** lyĕr′mŏn-tŏf.

REMEMBER THE ALAMO

Theodore Roosevelt

"THERMOPYLÆ had its messengers of death, but
the Alamo had none." These were the words
with which a United States senator referred to
one of the most resolute and effective fights ever
5 waged by brave men against overwhelming odds
in the face of certain death.

Soon after the close of the second war with Great
Britain, parties of American settlers began to press
forward into the rich, sparsely settled territory of
10 Texas, then a portion of Mexico. At first these
immigrants were well received, but the Mexicans
speedily grew jealous of them, and oppressed them
in various ways. In consequence, when the settlers
felt themselves strong enough, they revolted
15 against Mexican rule, and declared Texas to be
an independent republic. Immediately Santa
Anna, the dictator of Mexico, gathered a large
army and invaded Texas. The slender forces of
the settlers were unable to meet his hosts. They

Reprinted from Theodore Roosevelt's *Stories of the Great
West* by permission of The Century Co.

LINE **1.** **Thermopylæ** (thĕr-mŏp'ĭ-lē) : mountain pass between Thessaly and Greece famous for its defense by Leonidas.

were pressed back by the Mexicans, and dreadful atrocities were committed by Santa Anna and his lieutenants.

In the United States there was great enthusiasm for the struggling Texans, and many bold back- 5 woodsmen and Indian-fighters swarmed to their help. Among them the two most famous were Sam Houston and David Crockett. Houston was the younger man, and had already led an extraordinary and varied career. When a mere lad he ran 10 away from home and joined the Cherokees, living among them for some years; then he returned home. He had fought under Andrew Jackson in his campaigns against the Creeks, and had been severely wounded at the battle of the Horseshoe 15 Bend. He had risen to the highest political honors in his state, becoming governor of Tennessee; and then suddenly, in a fit of moody longing for the life of the wilderness, he gave up his governorship, left the state, and crossed the Mississippi, 20 going to join his old comrades, the Cherokees, in their new home along the waters of the Arkansas. Here he dressed, lived, fought, hunted, and drank precisely like any Indian, becoming one of the chiefs. 25

David Crockett was born soon after the Revolutionary War. He, too, had taken part under Jackson in the campaigns against the Creeks, and had afterward become a man of mark in Tennessee, and gone to Congress as a Whig; but he had quarreled with Jackson, and been beaten for Congress, and in his disgust he left the state and decided to join the Texans. He was the most famous rifle-shot in all the United States, and the most successful hunter, so that his skill was a proverb all along the border.

David Crockett journeyed south by boat and horse, making his way steadily toward the distant plains where the Texans were waging their life-and-death fight. Texas was a wild place in those days, and the old hunter had more than one hairbreadth escape from Indians, desperadoes, and savage beasts ere he got to the neighborhood of San Antonio, and joined another adventurer, a bee-hunter, bent on the same errand as himself. The two had been in ignorance of exactly what the situation in Texas was; but they soon found that the Mexican army was marching toward San Antonio, whither they were going. Near the town was an old Spanish fort, the Alamo, in which the hundred and fifty American defenders of the place had gathered. Santa Anna had four thousand troops with him. The Alamo was a mere shell, utterly unable to withstand either a bombardment or a regular assault. It was evident, therefore, that those within it would be in the utmost jeopardy if the place were seriously assaulted, but old Crockett and his companion never wavered. They were fearless and resolute, and masters of wood-craft, and they managed to slip through the Mexican lines and join the defenders within the walls. The bravest, the hardiest, the most reckless men of the border were there; among them were Colonel Travis, the commander of the fort, and Bowie, the inventor of the famous bowie knife. They were a wild and ill-disciplined band, little used to restraint or control, but they were men of iron courage and great bodily powers, skilled in the use of their weapons, and ready to meet with stern and uncomplaining indifference whatever doom fate might have in store for them.

Soon Santa Anna approached with his army, took possession of the town, and besieged the fort. The defenders knew there was scarcely a chance of rescue, and that it was hopeless to expect that one hundred and fifty men, behind defenses so weak, could beat off four thousand trained soldiers, well armed and provided with heavy artillery; but they had no idea of flinching, and made a desperate defense. The days went by, and no help came, while Santa Anna got ready his lines and began a furious cannonade. His gunners were unskilled, however, and he had to serve the guns from a distance; for when they were pushed nearer, the American riflemen crept forward under cover and picked off the artillerymen. Old Crockett thus killed five men at one gun. But, by degrees,

the bombardment told. The walls of the Alamo were battered and riddled; and when they had been breached so as to afford no obstacle to the rush of his soldiers, Santa Anna commanded that
5 they be stormed.

The storming took place on March 6, 1836. The Mexican troops came on well and steadily, breaking through the outer defenses at every point, for the lines were too long to be manned by the few Ameri-
10 cans. The frontiersmen then retreated to the inner building, and a desperate hand-to-hand conflict followed, the Mexicans thronging in, shooting the Americans with their muskets and thrusting at them with lance and bayonet, while the Ameri-
15 cans, after firing their long rifles, clubbed them and fought desperately, one against many; and they also used their bowie-knives and revolvers with deadly effect. The fight reeled to and fro between the shattered walls, each American the center of a
20 group of foes; but, for all their strength and their wild fighting courage, the defenders were too few, and the struggle could have but one end. One by one the tall riflemen succumbed, after repeated thrusts with bayonet and lance, until but three or
25 four were left. Colonel Travis, the commander, was among them; and so was Bowie, who was sick and weak from a wasting disease, but who rallied all his strength to die fighting, and who, in the final struggle, slew several Mexicans with his re-

volver, and with his big knife, of the kind to which he had given his name.

Then these fell, too, and the last man stood at bay. It was old Davy Crockett. Wounded in a dozen places, he faced his foes with his back to the wall, ringed round by the bodies of the men he had slain. So desperate was the fight he waged that the Mexicans who thronged round about him were beaten back for the moment, and no one dared to run in upon him. Accordingly, while the lancers held him where he was, for, weakened by wounds and loss of blood, he could not break through them, the musketeers loaded their carbines and shot him down. Santa Anna declined to give him mercy. Some say that when Crockett fell from his wounds, he was taken alive, and was then shot by Santa Anna's order; but his fate cannot be told with certainty, for not a single American was left alive. At any rate, after Crockett fell the fight was over. Every one of the hardy men who had held the Alamo lay still in death. Yet they died well avenged, for four times their number fell at their hands in the battle.

Santa Anna had but a short while in which to exult over the bloody and hard-won victory. Already a rider from the rolling Texas plains, going north through the Indian Territory, had told Houston that the Texans were up and were striving for their liberty. At once in Houston's mind there kindled a longing to return to the men of his race at the time of their need. Mounting his horse, he rode south by night and day, and was hailed by the Texans as a heaven-sent leader. He took command of their forces, eleven hundred stark riflemen, and at the battle of San Jacinto he and his men charged the Mexican hosts with the cry of "Remember the Alamo." Almost immediately the Mexicans were overthrown with terrible slaughter; Santa Anna himself was captured, and the freedom of Texas was won at a blow.

LINE **5.** **stark:** powerful.

THE ROOSEVELT SPIRIT IS NOT DEAD

Julian Street

He is a great man who is what he is from nature, and who never reminds us of others. — Emerson

WE, whom Theodore Roosevelt used proudly and affectionately to call his "fellow Americans," have always listened with great relish to characteristic stories of him. His qualities, physical and spiritual, were so utterly his own, his individuality 5 so intense and overmastering, that he seemed somehow to be projected among us, to be intimately known even to those of us who had never touched his hand or even seen him. It was this curious feeling as of personal acquaintance with him that 10 caused us so to delight in the flavor of a typical Roosevelt story.

"Isn't that just like him!" we would say, as we might of a story hitting off familiar traits of our own father. 15

But whereas, on the night of January 5, 1919, a Roosevelt story might by many of us have been regarded merely as something entertaining, the

Reprinted by permission of *Collier's, the National Weekly.*

next morning witnessed a great change. The wand
of Death, touching him gently as he slept, releasing
him to further high adventure, to great, final
explorations, transformed not him alone, but the
5 environment and the legend of him. To every
possession of his, from the wife and children he
loved to such small objects as that inkstand, made
from an elephant's foot, which stood upon his desk
at Sagamore Hill, or the very pens and pencils
10 there, thenceforth attached a quiet new sacredness.
And so, for us, his fellow Americans, new sacredness
attaches now to the rich legacy of wisdom he has left
us, to every thought of his that we can learn, to
every belief he held, and consequently to every
15 authentic story that can in any way contribute to
our knowledge of him.

In the vast amount of matter that has been
printed of the Colonel, I do not recall having seen
any reference to a certain theory that he had (and,
20 having it, of course he put it into practice) in connection with the bringing up of children. It was
a characteristic theory, and now it, like all else,
takes on a new significance.

As long since as when he was governor of New
25 York it was his practice to go every Saturday afternoon for a tramp in the country with Mrs. Roosevelt and the children. And it was understood

---

LINE **9.** **Sagamore Hill:** Roosevelt's home at Oyster Bay,
Long Island.

between them that in the course of all such tramps
he would lead them to some physical obstacle
which must be overcome. Sometimes it would
be merely the obstacle of long distance over a difficult terrain, calling for sustained effort in face of *s*
great fatigue; sometimes it would be a wide brook
to be crossed at a difficult place; sometimes a deep
ravine full of tangled underbrush to be traversed;
and on one memorable occasion, less than a fortnight before the Colonel was nominated for Vice- *1c*
President — that nomination designed by political
enemies within his own party to terminate his
political career — there was a steep cliff of crum-
bling slate to be ascended and descended.

The idea that Colonel and Mrs. Roosevelt at- *15*
tempted to fasten in the children's minds was that
life frequently presents obstacles comparable with
those encountered on these walks, and that it is the
part of good manhood and good womanhood
squarely to meet and surmount them, going through *20*
or over, but never around. Thus early the Roosevelt children, whose later record has been so worthy
of their father and their mother, had begun to
learn primary lessons in resourcefulness, persever-
ance, courage, stoicism, and disregard for danger — *25*
for sometimes, as in the adventure of the slate cliff,
there was danger.

LINE **5.** **terrain:** ground.   **25.** **stoicism:** self-control.

The Magic Spear

The bank, soft and almost perpendicular, at first appeared insurmountable, but after an hour and a half all but one of that day's walking party had managed to climb up and down again. The exception was Alice Roosevelt, then a girl of sixteen, who, having reached the top, found herself unable to descend.

On this day Elon Hooker, an old friend of the Roosevelts', was with them. Walking along the base of the cliff, this young man found a stout tree growing up beside it. Climbing the tree, he leaned out and, seizing with one hand a hummock of slate at the crest of the little precipice, offered his arm as a bridge over which Alice could step into the tree, whence it would be no very difficult matter to climb down to earth.

The hummock was less secure than it appeared. As she stepped upon his arm the slate to which he was holding broke away and his arm fell beneath her. She had, however, managed to grasp with one hand a branch, and to this she clung until he succeeded in catching her and drawing her safely into the tree.

In reaching the ground they discovered that the fallen mass of slate had struck the Colonel fairly on the head, laying open his scalp from the forehead to a corresponding point at the back of the skull. Though the wound bled freely, they were immediately reassured by his smile. Finding a brook, they washed the gash as best they could; later a surgeon took a dozen stitches in the Colonel's scalp; and when, some ten days later, he attended the Republican National Convention he was none the worse for the accident. Few persons, indeed, knew of it at all, for it was characteristic of him to avoid any mention of his injuries or ailments, and if forced to mention them he would invariably pass them off as being of no consequence.

Thus, for example, when it became known a twelve-month or so ago that he had been for many years stone blind in the left eye, as the result of a blow received in boxing, the news came as a surprise to numerous friends who knew him well. Yet he had been blind in that eye when he shot lions in Africa. He was not in the least sensitive about his blindness, nor do I think he tried particularly to conceal it. It was simply that he had an aversion, resembling that of the aboriginal American, for the discussion of bodily ills; a contempt for the inconvenience or suffering resulting from them. And still, when others suffered physically or spiritually, he was the most solicitous and gentlest, the tenderest of men.

It was like him, too, that throughout the afternoon on which he went to the hospital for a grave operation, a year ago, he continued to dictate

LINE **19.** aboriginal **American**: American Indian. **23.** solicitous: thoughtful.

letters to his secretary, and that while dictating he had a hemorrhage and fainted three times, only to revive and resume his dictation. And until the doctor forbade it, he even contemplated going that
5 night to a dinner at which he had agreed to speak.

On his hunting trips, when traveling, and more lately when confined to his bed in the hospital, he utilized every moment of his time for work, study, and reflection; he would concentrate upon a book
10 or a conversation while enduring pain to a degree that would have rendered it impossible for most men to think consecutively, much less converse upon important topics with a succession of visitors.

15 He was afraid neither to live nor to die. And in the purely orthodox sense he had no cause to fear death, for his soul was as clean as that of a little child. The ultimate biographer of Roosevelt will not have so much as one single item to gloss over or
20 conceal. And I am not sure that that is not the finest thing that may be said of any man.

Until a year ago I never heard him speak of death, but since then I have known him to speak of it more than once. I am wondering now if it merely hap-
25 pened so, or whether, as he lay there in the hospital a year ago, and again in the last months of the

---

Line **12.** **consecutively :** in logical order. **16.** **orthodox :** holding the commonly-accepted faith.

year just past, he may not have had a premonition that the end was perhaps nearer than those about him supposed. Certainly he knew a year ago, at the time of the operation for an abscess in the middle ear, which rapidly extended to the inner ear, that he was at death's door. Dr. Arthur B. Duel, his surgeon, told him so, and the Colonel promptly expressed a brave resignation.

I saw him in the hospital a few days after the operation. He was reading a book. After we had spoken a few words he said:

"Lying here, I have often thought how glad I would be to go now if by doing so I could only bring the boys back safe to Mrs. Roosevelt."

One day at luncheon last April, when we all thought him as vigorous as ever, he spoke again of his boys, and there was in what he said as much apprehension for them as he ever allowed himself to show — or perhaps I should say as much apprehension of the blow that the loss of any one of them would be to the remainder of the family.

"Mrs. Roosevelt has been perfectly wonderful," he said, "about their going to fight. We both realize that we have a very full, interesting, satisfying life to look back upon. Whatever may come now, we have had more than thirty years of happiness together, with all our children spared to us."

LINE **1.** **premonition :** forewarning.

And again, less than a month ago, as I write, when I called the hospital, Mrs. Roosevelt — who always stayed there with him — spoke in the same terms, though in the interim the blow had fallen.
5 It was of Quentin, the eagle, that she spoke.

"We have been until now a singularly united family," she said. "This is the first loss from our immediate circle. Life has been kind to us. We have much to be thankful for."

10 The story I have told of his walks with the children and the obstacles over which he led them was, until the morning of January 6, only a typical Roosevelt story. Since then it has become an allegory. For his feeling for us all was in a very 15 fine sense paternal. He was the father; we the children. "Face the obstacles," he always urged us. "Go through or over; never around."

Or to quote his own words, uttered in that great speech twenty years ago:

20 I preach to you, then, my countrymen, that our country calls not for the life of ease, but for the life of strenuous endeavor. The twentieth century looms before us big with the fate of many nations. If we stand idly by, if we seek merely swollen, slothful ease and ignoble peace, if we shrink 25 from the hard contests where men must win at hazard of their lives and at the risk of all they hold dear, then the bolder and stronger peoples will pass by us and will win for themselves the domination of the world.

LINE **14.** **allegory:** a story illustrating a truth.

The Roosevelt Spirit Is Not Dead

Let us therefore boldly face the life of strife, resolute to do our duty well and manfully; resolute to uphold righteousness by deed and by word; resolute to be both honest and brave, to serve high ideals, yet to use practical methods. Above all, let us not shrink from strife, moral or physical, within or without the nation, provided we are certain the strife is justified; for it is only through strife, through hard and dangerous endeavor, that we shall ultimately win the goal of true national greatness.

That, I believe, was the essence of Roosevelt's personal and national philosophy. Simply he thought and spoke and lived and died. And that, without exception, has been true of all our greatest men. Like Lincoln and Franklin, he was one of us. When he spoke we understood him. He never juggled thoughts or words to baffle us, confuse us, stupefy us with the brilliancy of his performance. Nor did he ever speak or write to mask a purpose or a lack of purpose. He never thought, as he tried to set down his ideas: "Now I am writing something that will live. Now I am making history." He was impatient of such notions, just as he was impatient of the applause that interrupted him when he was making public speeches. Time and again I have seen him hold up his hand to stop applause. He wanted to go on. It was the thing to be accomplished that obsessed him.

Thinking of the ingratitude that we have sometimes shown him, and of the follies we have committed, on occasion, in face of his exhortation to

245

be brave and prompt and ready, I once asked him
how he had kept from becoming cynical about
mankind.

"I am not cynical," he said, "because I have
5 observed that just when our people seem to be
becoming altogether hopeless they have a way of
suddenly turning around and doing something
perfectly magnificent."

Well may we be thankful that Roosevelt lived to
10 see his profound faith in us justified; to see us at
last take up arms in answer to his repeated call;
to see us quit the "life of ease" for that of
"strenuous endeavor"; to see us spurn "ignoble
peace" and enter the "hard contest where men must
15 win at hazard of their lives."

Thus his greatest single service to his country
was performed, not while he was President, but in
the last years of his life; not while he held the reins
of government, but as a private citizen whose un-
20 official power lay solely in the nation's admiration
for him; its faith in him and in his vision; its heed
to what he said.

There will, of course, be a memorial to Roosevelt.
It will be a noble thing of marble. But such a
25 thing, however glorious, will mean much more to
us than it could mean to him. We shall erect it to
give ourselves the mournful satisfaction of doing

LINE **2.** **cynical:** given to sneering because one thinks there
is nothing fine or good.

246

The Roosevelt Spirit Is Not Dead

our dead hero honor. But let us not forget, meanwhile, that the one memorial he would have wished cannot be built of tangible materials, but must be made of thoughts and deeds.

He has taken his last tramp with his own children, 5 and with us. He has guided them, and us, up to the last obstacle we were destined to meet and overcome under his leadership. And the one thing he would ask of us is this: That we go on without him. That we learn the simple lessons he has 10 taught by precept and example. That we be foresighted, prompt, practical, honest, resolute, courageous.

So, in ourselves, we will make his spirit live.

LINE **3.** **tangible:** perceptible to the senses; real.

I MEET A LION

David Livingstone

RETURNING toward Kuruman, I selected the beautiful valley of Mabotsa as the site of a missionary station; and thither I removed in 1843. Here an occurrence took place, concerning which I have 5 frequently been questioned in England, and which, but for the importunities of friends, I meant to have kept in store to tell my children when in my dotage. The Bakatla of the village Mabotsa were much troubled by lions, which leaped into the 10 cattle pens by night and destroyed their cows. They even attacked the herds in open day. This was so unusual an occurrence that the people believed that they were bewitched — "given," as they said, "into the power of the lions by a neigh-15 boring tribe." They went once to attack the animals, but, being a rather cowardly people compared to Bechuanas in general on such occasions, they returned without killing any.

It is well known that if one in a troop of lions is 20 killed, the others take the hint, and leave that part

LINE 1. **Kuruman:** an African village. **8. Bakatla:** an African tribe. **17. Bechuanas:** an African tribe.

of the country. So the next time the herds were attacked, I went with the people, in order to encourage them to rid themselves of the annoyance by destroying one of the marauders. We found the lions on a small hill, about a quarter of a mile 5 in length, and covered with trees. A circle of men was formed round it, and they gradually closed up, ascending pretty near to each other. Being down below on the plain with a native schoolmaster, named Mebalwe, a most excellent man, I saw one 10 of the lions sitting on a piece of rock within the now closed circle of men. Mebalwe fired at him before I could, and the ball struck the rock on which the animal was sitting. He bit at the spot struck, as a dog does at a stick or stone thrown at him; 15 then leaping away, broke through the opening circle and escaped unhurt. The men were afraid to attack him, perhaps on account of their belief in witchcraft. When the circle was re-formed, we saw two other lions in it; but we were afraid to 20 fire, lest we should strike the men, and they allowed the beasts to burst through also. If the Bakatla had acted according to the custom of the country, they would have speared the lions in their attempt to get out. Seeing we could not get them to kill 25 one of the lions, we bent our footsteps toward the village; in going round the end of the hill, however,

---

LINE **4. marauders:** robbers.

The Magic Spear

I saw one of the beasts sitting on a piece of rock as before, but this time he had a little bush in front. Being about thirty yards off, I took a good aim at his body through the bush, and fired both barrels 5 into it. The men then called out, "He is shot, he is shot!" Others cried, "He has been shot by another man, too; let us go to him!" I did not see any one else shoot at him, but I saw the lion's tail erected in anger behind the bush, and, turning 10 to the people, said, "Stop a little till I load again!" When in the act of ramming down the bullets I heard a shout.

Starting and looking half round, I saw the lion just in the act of springing upon me. I was upon a 15 little height; he caught my shoulder as he sprang, and we both came to the ground below together. Growling horribly close to my ear, he shook me as a terrier dog does a rat. This shock produced a stupor similar to that which seems to be felt by a 20 mouse after the first shake of the cat. It caused a sort of dreaminess, in which there was no sense of pain, nor feeling of terror, though I was quite conscious of all that was happening. It was like what patients partially under the influence of chloroform 25 describe, who see the operation, but feel not the knife. This singular condition was not the result of any mental process. The shake annihilated fear,

---

LINE **24.** **chloroform:** an anesthetic.

and allowed no sense of horror in looking round at
the beast.   This peculiar state is probably produced
in all animals killed by the carnivora; and, if so,
is a merciful provision by our benevolent Creator
for lessening the pain of death.   5

Turning round to relieve myself of the weight,
as he had one paw on the back of my head, I saw
his eyes directed toward Mebalwe, who was trying
to shoot him at a distance of ten or fifteen yards.
His gun, a flint one, missed fire in both barrels; the 10
lion immediately left me, and, attacking Mebalwe,
bit his thigh. Another man, whose life I had
saved before, after he had been tossed by a buffalo,
attempted to spear the lion while he was biting
Mebalwe.   He left Mebalwe and caught this man 15
by the shoulder, but at this moment the bullets
he had received took effect, and he fell down dead.
The whole was the work of a few minutes, and must
have been his paroxysm of dying rage.   In order to
take out the charm from him, the Bakatla on the 20
following day made a huge bonfire over the carcass,
which was declared to be that of the largest lion
they had ever seen. Besides crunching the bone
into splinters, he left eleven teeth wounds on the
upper part of my arm.   A wound from this animal's 25
tooth resembles a gun-shot wound; it is generally
followed by a great deal of sloughing and discharge,

LINE **3.** **carnivora:** flesh-eating animals.   **19.** **paroxysm:**
a convulsion or fit.

and pains are felt periodically ever afterward. I had on a tartan jacket on the occasion, and I believe that it wiped off all the virus from the teeth that pierced the flesh, for my two companions in this affray have both suffered from the peculiar pains, while I have escaped with only the inconvenience of a false joint in the limb. The man whose shoulder was wounded showed me his wound actually burst forth afresh on the same month of the following year. This curious point deserves the attention of inquirers.

LINE **2.** **tartan:** Scotch plaid woolen fabric.

HOW TO GET THE BEST OUT
OF BOOKS

Richard Le Gallienne

ONE is sometimes asked by young people panting
after the water brooks of knowledge: "How shall
I get the best out of books?" Here, indeed, is one
of those questions which can be answered only in
general terms, with possible illustrations from 5
one's own personal experience. Misgivings, too,
as to one's fitness to answer it may well arise, as
wistfully looking round one's own bookshelves,
one asks oneself: "Have I myself got the best out
of books?" It is almost like asking oneself: 10
"Have I got the best out of life?"

As we make the survey, it will surely happen that
our eyes fall on many writers whom the stress of
life, or spiritual indolence, has prevented us from
using as all the while they have been eager to be 15
used; friends we might have made yet have never
made, neglected counselors we would so often have
done well to consult, guides that could have saved
us many a wrong turning in the difficult way.
There, in unvisited corners of our shelves, what 20
neglected fountains of refreshment, gardens in

The Magic Spear

which we have never walked, hills we have never climbed!

"Well," we say with a sigh, "a man cannot read everything; it is life that has interrupted our 5 studies, and probably the fact is that we have accumulated more books than we really need." The young reader's appetite is largely in his eyes, and it is very natural for one who is born with a taste for books to gather them about him at first 10 indiscriminately, on the hearsay recommendation of fame, before he really knows what his own individual tastes are, or are going to be, and, in that wistful survey I have imagined, our eyes will fall, too, with some amusement, on not a few volumes 15 to which we never have had any really personal relation, and which, whatever their distinction or their value for others, were never meant for us. The way to do with such books is to hand them over to some one who has a use for them. On our 20 shelves they are like so much good thrown away, invitations to entertainments for which we have no taste. In all vital libraries, such a process of progressive refection is continually going on, and to realize what we do not want in books, or cannot 25 use, must, obviously, be a first principle in our getting the best out of them.

Yes, we read too many books, and too many

LINE **10.** **indiscriminately:** haphazard; without judgment. **22.** **vital:** living. **23.** **refection:** refreshment by food.

254

that, as they do not really interest us, bring us
neither benefit nor diversion. Even from the point
of view of reading for pleasure, we manage our
reading badly. We listlessly allow ourselves to be
bullied by publishers' advertisements into reading 5
the latest fatuity in fiction, without, in one case
out of twenty, finding any of that pleasure we are
ostensibly seeking. Instead, indeed, we are bored
and enervated, where we might have been refreshed,
either by romance or by laughter. Such reading 10
resembles the idle absorption of innocuous but
uninteresting beverages, which cheer as little as
they inebriate, and yet at the same time make
frivolous demands on the digestive functions. No
one but a publisher could call such reading "light." 15
Actually it is weariness of the flesh and heaviness
of the spirit.

If, therefore, our idea of the best in books is the
recreation they can so well bring, if we go to books
as to a playground to forget our cares, and to blow 20
off the cobwebs of business, let us make sure that
we find what we seek. It is there surely enough.
The playgrounds of literature are indeed wide, and
alive with bracing excitement, nor is there any limit
to the variety of the games. But let us be sure, 25
when we set out to be amused, that we are really
amused, that our humorists do really make us laugh,

LINE **11.** **innocuous:** harmless.

and that our story-tellers have stories to tell and know how to tell them. Beware of imitations, and, when in doubt, try Shakespeare, and Dumas — even Ouida. As a rule, avoid the "spring lists,"
5 or "summer reading." "Summer reading" is usually very hot work.

Hackneyed as it is, there is no better general advice on reading than Shakespeare's

> No profit is where is no pleasure taken;
> 10 In brief, sir, study what you most affect.

Not only in regard to books whose purpose, frankly, is recreation, but also in regard to the graver uses of books, this counsel no less holds. No reading does us any good that is not a pleasure
15 to us. Her paths are paths of pleasantness. Yet, of course, this does not mean that all profitable reading is easy reading. Some of the books that give us the finest pleasure need the closest application for their enjoyment. There is always a
20 certain spiritual and mental effort necessary to be made before we tackle the great books. One might compare it to the effort of getting up to see the sun rise. It is no little of a tug to leave one's warm bed — but once we are out in the crystalline
25 morning air, wasn't it worth it? Perhaps our finest pleasure always demands some such austerity

---

LINE **4**. **Ouida** (wē′dà): an Anglo-French novelist — Louise de la Ramée.

of preparation. That is the secret of the truest
epicureanism. Books like Dante's *Divine Comedy*
or Plato's dialogues will not give themselves to a
lounging reader. They demand a braced, attentive
spirit. But when the first effort has been made, 5
how exhilarating are the altitudes in which we find
ourselves, what a glow of pure joy is the reward
which we are almost sure to win by our mental
mountaineering.

But such books are not for moments when we are 10
unwilling or unable to make that necessary effort.
We cannot always be in the mood for the great
books, and often we are too tired physically, or too
low down on the depressed levels of daily life, even
to lift our eyes toward the hills. To attempt the 15
great books — or any books at all — in such moods
and moments, is a mistake. We may thus con-
tract a prejudice against some writer who, approached in more fortunate moments, would prove
the very man we were looking for.   20

To know when to read is hardly less important
than to know what to read. Of course, every one
must decide the matter for himself, but one general
counsel may be ventured : Read only what you
want to read, and only when you want to read it. 25

Some readers find the early morning, when they
have all the world to themselves, their best time

LINE **2. epicureanism:** delicacy of taste.

for reading, and, if you are a good sleeper, and do not find early rising more wearying than refreshing, there is certainly no other time of the day when the mind is so eagerly receptive, has so keen an 5 edge of appetite, and absorbs a book in so fine an intoxication. For your true book-lover there is no other exhilaration so exquisite as that with which one reads an inspiring book in the solemn freshness of early morning. One's nerves seem peculiarly 10 strung for exquisite impressions in the first dewy hours of the day; there are a virginal sensitiveness and a purity about all our senses, and the mere delight of the eye in the printed page is keener than at any other time. "The Muses love the 15 morning, and that is a fit time for study," said Erasmus to his friend Christianus of Lübeck; and, certainly, if early rising agrees with one, there is no better time for getting the very best out of a book. Moreover, morning reading has a way of 20 casting a spell of peace over the whole day. It has a sweet, solemnizing effect on our thoughts — a sort of mental matins — and through the day's business it accompanies us as with hidden music.

There are other readers who prefer to do their 25 reading at night, and I presume that most readers of this paper are so circumstanced as to have no time to spare for reading during the day. Person-

---

Line **16**.   **Erasmus:** a Dutch scholar of the Middle Ages.

258

ally, I think that one of the best places to read is in bed. Paradoxical as it may sound, one is not so apt to fall asleep over his book in bed as in the post-prandial armchair. While one's body rests itself, one's mind remains alert, and, when the time for 5 sleep comes at last, it passes into unconsciousness, tranquilized and sweetened with thought and pleasantly weary with healthy exercise. One awakens, too, next morning, with, so to say, a very pleasant taste of meditation in the mouth. 10 Erasmus, again, has a counsel for the bedtime reader, expressed with much felicity. "A little before you sleep," he says, "read something that is exquisite, and worth remembering; and contemplate upon it till you fall asleep; and, when you 15 awake in the morning, call yourself to an account for it."

In an old *Atlantic Monthly*, from which, if I remember aright, he never rescued it, Oliver Wendell Holmes has a delightful paper on the de- 20 lights of reading in bed, entitled *Pillow-Smoothing Authors*.

Then, though I suppose we shall have the ocu-lists against us, the cars are good places to read in — if you have the power of detachment, and are 25 able to switch off your ears from other people's conversation. It is a good plan to have a book with

LINE **2. Paradoxical:** absurd. **3. postprandial:** after-dinner.

you in all places and at all times. Most likely you
will carry it many a day and never give it a single
look, but, even so, a book in the hand is always a
companionable reminder of that happier world of
5 fancy, which, alas! most of us can visit only by
playing truant from the real world. As some men
wear *boutonnières*, so a reader carries a book, and
sometimes, when he is feeling the need of beauty,
or the solace of a friend, he opens it, and finds
10 both. Probably he will count among the most
fruitful moments of his reading the snatched
glimpses of beauty and wisdom he has caught in
the morning car. The covers of his books have
often proved like some secret door, through which,
15 surreptitiously opened, he has looked for a moment
into his own particular fairyland. Never mind
the oculist, therefore, but, whenever you feel like
it, read in the car.

One or two technical considerations may be
20 dealt with in this place. How to remember what
one reads is one of them. Some people are blest
with such good memories that they never forget
anything that they have once read. Literary
history has recorded many miraculous memories.
25 Still, it is quite possible to remember too much,
and thus turn one's mind into a lumber room of
useless information. A good reader forgets even

LINE **7.** *boutonnières:* buttonhole bouquets. **15. surreptitiously:** slyly.

more than he remembers.   Probably we remember
all that is really necessary for us, and, except in so
far as our reading is technical and directed toward
some exact science or profession, accuracy of
memory is not important.   As the Sabbath was 5
made for man, so books were made for the reader,
and, when a reader has assimilated from any given
book his own proper nourishment and pleasure,
the rest of the book is so much oyster shell.   The
end of true reading is the development of individ- 10
uality.   Like a certain water insect, the reader
instinctively selects from the outspread world of
books the building materials for the house of his
soul.   He chooses here and rejects there, and
remembers or forgets according to the formative 15
desire of his nature.   Yet it often happens that he
forgets much that he needs to remember, and
thus the question of methodical aids to memory
arises.

One's first thought, of course, is of the common- 20
place book.   Well, have you ever kept one, or,
to be more accurate, tried to keep one?   Person-
ally, I believe in the commonplace book so long as
we don't expect too much from it.   Its two dangers
are (1) that one is apt to make far too many and too 25
minute entries, and (2) that one is apt to leave all
the remembering to the commonplace book, with
the consequent relaxation of one's own attention.
On the other hand, the mere discipline of a

commonplace book is a good thing, and if — as I
think is the best way — we copy out the passages
at full length, they are thus the more securely fixed
in the memory. A commonplace book kept with
5 moderation is really useful, and may be delightful.
But the entries should be made at full length.
Otherwise, the thing becomes a mere index, an
index which encourages us to forget.

Another familiar way of assisting one's memory
10 in reading is to mark one's own striking passages.
This method is chiefly worth while for the sake of
one's second and subsequent readings; though it
all depends on when one makes the markings — at
what time of his life, I mean. Markings made
15 at the age of twenty years are of little use at thirty
— except negatively. In fact, I have usually
found that all I care to read again of a book read
at twenty is just the passages I did not mark.
This consideration, however, does not depreciate
20 the value of one's comparatively contemporary
markings. At the same time, marking, like index-
ing, is apt, unless guarded against, to relax the
memory. One is apt to mark a passage in lieu of
remembering it. Still, for a second reading, as I
25 say — a second reading not too long after the first
— marking is a useful method, particularly if one

LINE **1**. **commonplace book:** a notebook in which one
jots down quotations from books read. **20. contemporary:**
of the same time.

regards his first reading of a book as a prospecting of the ground rather than a taking possession. One's first reading is a sort of flying visit, during which he notes the places he would like to visit again and really come to know. A brief index of one's markings at the end of a volume is a method of memory that commended itself to the booklovers of former days — to Leigh Hunt, for instance.

Yet none of these external methods, useful as they may prove, can compare with a habit of thorough attention. We read far too hurriedly, too much in the spirit of the "quick lunch." No doubt we do so a great deal from the misleading idea that there is so very much to read. Actually, there is very little to read — if we wish for real reading — and there is time to read it all over twice. We — Americans — bolt our books as we do our food, and so get far too little good out of them. We treat our mental digestions as brutally as we treat our stomachs. Meditation is the digestion of the mind, but we allow ourselves no time for meditation. We gorge our eyes with the printed page, but all too little of what we take in with our eyes ever reaches our minds or our spirits. We assimilate what we can from all this hurry of superfluous food, and the rest goes to waste, and, as a natural consequence, contributes only to the wear and tear of our mental organism.

Books should be real things. They were so once,

when a man would give a fat field in exchange for a small manuscript; and they are no less real to-day — some of them.   Each age contributes one or two real books to the eternal library — and always the
5 old books remain, magic springs of healing and refreshment.   If no one should write a book for a thousand years, there are quite enough books to keep us going.   Real books there are in plenty. Perhaps there are more real books than there are
10 real readers.   Books are the strong tincture of experience.   They are to be taken carefully, drop by drop, not carelessly gulped down by the bottle. Therefore, if you would get the best out of books, spend a quarter of an hour in reading, and three
15 quarters of an hour in thinking over what you have read.

LINE **10.** **tincture:** extract.

THE GAME OF LIFE

SUPPOSE it were perfectly certain that the life and fortune of every one of us would, one day or other, depend upon his winning or losing a game of chess. Don't you think that we should all consider it to be a primary duty to learn at least the names and the 5 moves of the pieces; to have a notion of a gambit, and a keen eye for all the means of giving and getting out of check? Do you not think that we should look with a disapprobation amounting to scorn upon the father who allowed his son, or the 10 state which allowed its members, to grow up without knowing a pawn from a knight?

Yet it is very plain and elementary truth that the life, the fortune, and the happiness of every one of us, and, more or less, of those who are connected 15 with us, do depend upon our knowing something of the rules of a game infinitely more difficult and

---

Reprinted from *Science and Education* by Thomas H. Huxley, copyrighted by D. Appleton &] Company, New York.

LINE **6.** **gambit:** a chess opening in which the first player loses a man for advantage in position. **8.** **out of check:** a chess term. **12.** **pawn:** a chess man. **knight:** a chess man.

complicated than chess. It is a game which has been played for untold ages, every man and woman of us being one of the two players in a game of his or her own. The chessboard is the world, the pieces are the phenomena of the universe, the rules of the the game are what we call the laws of nature. The player on the other side is hidden from us. We know that his play is always fair, just, and patient. But we also know, to our cost, that he never overlooks a mistake, or makes the smallest allowance for ignorance. To the man who plays well, the highest stakes are paid, with that sort of overflowing generosity with which the strong shows delight in strength. And one who plays ill is checkmated — without haste but without remorse.

My metaphor will remind some of you of the famous picture in which Retzsch has depicted Satan playing at chess with man for his soul. Substitute for that mocking fiend in that picture a calm, strong angel who is playing for love, as we say, and would rather lose than win — and I should accept it as an image of human life.

Well, what I mean by education is learning the rules of this mighty game. In other words, education is the instruction of the intellect in the laws of nature, under which name I include not merely things and their forces, but men and their ways;

LINE **16.** **metaphor:** a figure of speech. **17.** **Retzsch:** a German painter and etcher.

and the fashioning of the affections and of the will into an earnest and loving desire to move in harmony with those laws. For me, education means neither more nor less than this. Anything which professes to call itself education must be tried by this standard, and if it fails to stand the test, I will not call it education, whatever may be the force of authority, or of numbers, upon the other side.

THE KING'S JEWEL

Henry van Dyke

THERE was an outcry at the door of the king's great hall, and suddenly a confusion arose. The guards ran thither swiftly, and the people were crowded together, pushing and thrusting as if to
5 withhold some intruder. Out of the tumult came a strong voice shouting, "I will come in! I must see the false king!" But other voices cried, "Not so — you are mad — you shall not come in thus!"

Then the king said, "Let him come in as he will!"
10 So the confusion fell apart, and the hall was very still, and a man in battered armor stumbled through the silence and stood in front of the throne. He was breathing hard, for he was weary and angry and afraid, and the sobbing of his breath shook him
15 from head to foot. But his anger was stronger than his weariness and his fear; so he lifted his eyes hardily and looked the king in the face.

It was like the face of a mountain, very calm and very high, but not unkind. When the man saw it
20 clearly he knew that he was looking at the true

The man drew from his breast a golden chain.

king; but his anger was not quenched, and he stood stiff, with drawn brows, until the king said, "Speak!"

For answer the man drew from his breast a golden chain, at the end of which was a jewel set with a great blue stone. He looked at it for a moment with scorn, as one who had a grievance. Then he threw it down on the steps of the throne, and turned on his heel to go.

"Stay," said the king. "Whose is this jewel?"

"I thought it to be yours," said the man.

"Where did you get it?" asked the king.

"From an old servant of yours," answered the man. "He gave it to me when I was but a lad, and told me it came from the king — it was the blue stone of Truth, perfect and priceless. Therefore I must keep it as the apple of mine eye, and bring it back to the king perfect and unbroken."

"And you have done this?" said the king.

"Yes and no," answered the man.

"Divide your answer," said the king. "First, the *yes*."

The man delayed a moment before he spoke. Then his words came slow and firm as if they were measured and weighed in his mind.

"All that man could do, O king, have I done to keep this jewel of the Truth. Against open foes and secret robbers I have defended it, with faithful watching and hard fighting. Through storm and

269

peril, through darkness and sorrow, through the temptation of pleasure and the bewilderment of riches, I have never parted from it. Gold could not buy it; passion could not force it; nor man nor woman could wile or win it away. Glad or sorry, well or wounded, at home or in exile, I have given my life to keep the jewel. This is the meaning of the *yes*."

"It is right," said the king. "And now the *no*."

The man answered quickly and with heat.

"The *no* is right also, O king! But not by my fault. The jewel is not untarnished, not perfect. It never was. There is a flaw in the stone. I saw it first when I entered the light of your palace gate. Look, it is marred and imperfect, a thing of little value. It is not the crystal of Truth. I have been deceived. You have claimed my life for a fool's errand, a thing of naught; no jewel, but a bauble. Take it. It is yours."

The king looked not at the gold chain and the blue stone, but at the face of the man. He looked quietly and kindly and steadily into the eyes full of pain and wounded loyalty, until they fell before his look. Then he spoke gently.

"Will you give me my jewel?"

The man lifted his eyes in wonder.

"It is there," he cried, "at your feet!"

"I spoke not of that," said the king, "but of your life, yourself."

The King's Jewel

"My life," said the man faltering, "what is that? Is it not ended?"

"It is begun," said the king. "Your life — yourself, what of that?"

"I had not thought of that," said the man; "only of the jewel, not of myself, my life."

"Think of it now," said the king, "and think clearly. Have you not learned courage and hardiness? Have not your labors brought you strength; your perils, wisdom; your wounds, patience? Has not your task broken chains for you, and lifted you out of sloth and above fear? Do you say that the stone that has done this for you is false, a thing of naught?"

"Is this true?" said the man, trembling and sinking on his knee.

"It is true," answered the king; "as God lives, it is true. Come, stand at my right hand. My jewels that I seek are not dead, but alive. But the stone which led you here — look! has it a flaw?"

He stooped and lifted the jewel. The light of his face fell upon it. And in the blue depths of the sapphire the man saw a star.

SPINNING OUR FATES

William James

WE are spinning our own fates, good or evil, never
to be undone. Every smallest stroke of virtue or
vice leaves its never-so-little scar. The drunken
Rip Van Winkle, in Jefferson's play, excuses himself
5 for every fresh dereliction by saying, "I won't count
this time!" Well, he may not count it, and a kind
Heaven may not count it; but it is being counted
none the less. Down among his nerve cells and
fibers the molecules are counting it, registering and
10 storing it up to be used against him when the next
temptation comes. Nothing we ever do is, in strict
scientific literalness, wiped out.

Of course, this has its good side as well as its
bad one. As we become permanent drunkards
15 by so many separate drinks, so we become saints
in the moral, and authorities and experts in the
practical and scientific spheres, by so many separate
acts and hours of work. Let no youth have any
anxiety about the upshot of his education, whatever

Reprinted from William James' *Talks to Teachers* by permission of Henry Holt and Company.
LINE **5.** **dereliction:** failure in duty.

the line of it may be. If he keep faithfully busy
each hour of the working day, he may safely leave
the final result to itself. He can with perfect
certainty count on waking up some fine morning to
find himself one of the competent ones of his gen- 5
eration in whatever pursuit he may have singled out.
Silently, between all the details of his business, the
power of judging in all that class of matter will
have built itself up within him as a possession that
will never pass away. Young people should know 10
this truth in advance. The ignorance of it has
probably engendered more discouragement and
faint-heartedness in youths embarking on arduous
careers than all other causes put together.

Line **12.** **engendered:** created.

WHAT IS LIBERTY?

Woodrow Wilson

WHAT is liberty?

I have long had an image in my mind of what
constitutes liberty.   Suppose that I were building a
great piece of powerful machinery, and suppose that
5 I should so awkwardly and unskillfully assemble
the parts of it that, every time one part tried to
move, it would be interfered with by the others, and
the whole thing would buckle up and be checked.
Liberty for the several parts would consist in the
10 best possible assembling and adjustment of them
all, would it not?   If you want the great piston of
the engine to run with absolute freedom, give it
absolutely perfect alignment and adjustment with
the other parts of the machine, so that it is free,
15 not because it is let alone or isolated, but because
it has been associated most skillfully and carefully
with the other parts of the great structure.

What is liberty? You say of the locomotive
that it runs free.   What do you mean?   You mean

Reprinted from *The New Freedom* by Woodrow Wilson, published by Doubleday, Doran and Company.
LINE **8.** **buckle up:** bend.   **13.** **alignment:** arrangement.

that its parts are so assembled and adjusted that
friction is reduced to a minimum, and that it has
perfect adjustment. We say of a boat skimming
the water with light foot, "How free she runs,"
when we mean, how perfectly she is adjusted to the 5
force of the wind, how perfectly she obeys the great
breath out of the heavens that fills her sails. Throw
her head up into the wind and see how she will halt
and stagger, how every sheet will shiver and her
whole frame be shaken, how instantly she is "in 10
irons," in the expressive phrase of the sea. She is
free only when you have let her fall off again and
have recovered once more her nice adjustment to
the forces she must obey and cannot defy.

Human freedom consists in perfect adjustments 15
of human interests and human activities and human
energies.

Now, the adjustments necessary between individuals, between individuals and the complex institutions amid which they live, and between those 20
institutions and the government, are infinitely
more intricate to-day than ever before. No doubt
this is a tiresome and roundabout way of saying the
thing, yet perhaps it is worth while to get somewhat
clearly in our mind what makes all the trouble 25
to-day. Life has become complex; there are
many more elements, more parts, to it than ever

LINE **2.** **minimum:** least amount.

before. And, therefore, it is harder to keep everything adjusted — and harder to find out where the trouble lies when the machine gets out of order.

5 You know that one of the interesting things that Mr. Jefferson said in those early days of simplicity which marked the beginnings of our government was that the best government consisted in as little governing as possible. And there is still a sense in 10 which that is true. It is still intolerable for the government to interfere with our individual activities except where it is necessary to interfere with them in order to free them. But I feel confident that if Jefferson were living in our day he would see 15 what we see: that the individual is caught in a great confused nexus of all sorts of complicated circumstances, and that to let him alone is to leave him helpless as against the obstacles with which he has to contend; and that, therefore, law in our 20 day must come to the assistance of the individual. It must come to his assistance to see that he gets fair play; that is all, but that is much. Without the watchful interference, the resolute interference, of the government, there can be no fair play between 25 individuals and such powerful institutions as the trusts. Freedom to-day is something more than being let alone. The program of a government of

---

LINE **16.** **nexus:** bond or tie.

freedom must in these days be positive, not negative merely.

Well, then, in this new sense and meaning of it, are we preserving freedom in this land of ours, the hope of all the earth? 5

Have we, inheritors of this continent and of the ideals to which the fathers consecrated it — have we maintained them, realizing them, as each generation must, anew? Are we, in the consciousness that the life of man is pledged to higher levels here 10 than elsewhere, striving still to bear aloft the standards of liberty and hope, or, disillusioned and defeated, are we feeling the disgrace of having had a free field in which to do new things and of not having done them? 15

In all that I may have to do in public affairs in the United States I am going to think of towns such as I have seen in Indiana, towns of the old American pattern, that own and operate their own industries, hopefully and happily. My thought is going to be 20 bent upon the multiplication of towns of that kind and the prevention of the concentration of industry in this country in such a fashion and upon such a scale that towns that own themselves will be impossible. You know what the vitality of 25 America consists of. Its vitality does not lie in New York, nor in Chicago; it will not be sapped by anything that happens in St. Louis. The vitality of America lies in the brains, the energies, the enterprise of the people throughout the land; in the efficiency of their factories and in the richness of the fields that stretch beyond the borders of the town; in the wealth which they extract from nature and originate for themselves through the inventive genius characteristic of all free American communities.

That is the wealth of America, and if America discourages the locality, the community, the self-contained town, she will kill the nation. A nation is as rich as her free communities; she is not as rich as her capital city or her metropolis.

We have carried in our minds, after you had thought you had obscured and blurred them, the ideals of those men who first set their foot upon America, those little bands who came to make a foothold in the wilderness, because the great teeming nations that they had left behind them had forgotten what human liberty was, liberty of thought, liberty of religion, liberty of residence, liberty of action.

Since their day the meaning of liberty has deepened. But it has not ceased to be a fundamental demand of the human spirit, a fundamental necessity for the life of the soul. And the day is at hand when it shall be realized on this consecrated soil — a New Freedom — a liberty widened and deepened to match the broadened life of man in modern America, restoring to him in very truth the control

278

of his government, throwing wide all gates of lawful enterprise, unfettering his energies, and warming the generous impulses of his heart — a process of release, emancipation, and inspiration, full of a breath of life as sweet and wholesome as the airs 5 that filled the sails of the caravels of Columbus and gave the promise and boast of magnificent opportunity in which America *dare not fail*.

CADET PRAYER

Clayton E. Wheat

O GOD, our Father, Thou Searcher of men's hearts, help us to draw near to Thee in sincerity and truth. May our religion be filled with gladness and may our worship of Thee be natural.

5 Strengthen and increase our admiration for honest dealing and clean thinking, and suffer not our hatred of hypocrisy and pretense ever to diminish. Encourage us in our endeavor to live above the common level of life. Make us to choose the
10 harder right instead of the easier wrong, and never to be content with a half truth when the whole can be won. Endow us with courage that is born of loyalty to all that is noble and worthy, that scorns to compromise with vice and injustice and knows
15 no fear when truth and right are in jeopardy. Guard us against flippancy and irreverence in the sacred things of life. Grant us new ties of friendship and new opportunities of service. Kindle our hearts in fellowship with those of a cheerful coun-
20 tenance, and soften our hearts with sympathy for those who sorrow and suffer. May we find genuine pleasure in clean and wholesome mirth and feel

Cadet Prayer

inherent disgust for all coarse-minded humor. Help us, in our work and in our play, to keep ourselves physically strong, mentally awake, and morally straight, that we may the better maintain the honor of the Corps untarnished and unsullied, 5 and acquit ourselves like men in our effort to realize the ideals of West Point in doing our duty to Thee and to our Country. All of which we ask in the name of the Great Friend and Master of men. Amen. 10

A CODE OF CITIZENSHIP

Henry B. Wilson

[The Naval Academy at Annapolis tries to impress the entering midshipmen with a few fundamental principles of conduct. This is the sort of talk that Admiral Henry B. Wilson, Superintendent, gives the students who are eventually to command our fleet.]

FIRST, a naval officer tells the truth regardless of the consequences to himself, and he scorns the appearance of untruth or evasion.

Second, in the navy the task must be accom-
5 plished. No matter how hard it is, never come back and say, "I could not do it." Obstacles are things to climb over, not turn back from.

Third, profanity is not allowed here. Worse than profanity is the use of unclean language. It
10 does not form part of the vocabulary of an officer or of a gentleman anywhere. Tie up to those who do not use that kind; don't use it yourself; and in a quiet way discourage others.

Fourth, an officer does not steal or cheat. Never,
15 through a mistaken sense of kindness or loyalty to another midshipman, protect one who is a thief. There is no place in the Naval Academy or in the navy for such.

A Code of Citizenship

Fifth, keep clean. Every room has a shower. Get the habit. You will feel better for it all day. When you get on board ship, you will find that this is the first thing that an officer does each morning.

Sixth, it is one of our traditions that a man fights 5 to the last. That does not mean that you must look for trouble, but it does mean that you must not quit.

There are many other elements of character of which I will talk to your whole class later. 10

The oath says that you will support and defend the Constitution against enemies — foreign and domestic. Domestic enemies are people within our country who try to break down the strong government your ancestors and mine founded. 15 There is no place for them here. . . .

Party politics do not concern you. When the country has chosen a government, our loyalty and obedience are to that government. Never be disloyal to your country, to the navy, or to your 20 officers, and do not permit others to be disloyal in your presence. This will be bearing true faith and allegiance.

TO HIS DAUGHTER

William James

Villa Luise
Bad-Nauheim, May 26, 1900

DARLING PEG,

Your letter came last night and explained sufficiently the cause of your long silence. You have
evidently been in a bad state of spirits again, and
dissatisfied with your environment; and I judge
that you have been still more dissatisfied with the
inner state of trying to consume your own smoke,
and grin and bear it, so as to carry out your mother's
behests made after the time when you scared us so
by your inexplicable tragic outcries in those earlier
letters. Well! I believe you have been trying to
do the manly thing under difficult circumstances,
but one learns only gradually to do the *best* thing;
and the best thing for you would be to write at
least weekly, if only a postcard, and say just how
things are going. If you are in bad spirits, there is
no harm whatever in communicating that fact, and

Reprinted from *The Letters of William James* by permission of Little, Brown and Company.

defining the character of it, or describing it as
exactly as you like. The bad thing is to pour out
the *content* of one's bad spirits on others and leave
them with it, as it were, on their hands, as if it were
for them to do something about it. That was 5
what you did in your other letter which alarmed us
so, for your shrieks of anguish were so excessive, and
so unexplained by anything you told us in the way
of facts, that we didn't know but what you had
suddenly gone crazy. That is the *worst* sort of 10
thing you can do. The middle sort of thing is what
you do this time — namely, keep silent for more
than a fortnight, and when you do write. still write
rather mysteriously about your sorrows, not being
quite open enough.   15

Now, my dear little girl, you have come to an age
when the inward life develops and when some
people (and on the whole those who have most of a
destiny) find that all is not a bed of roses. Among
other things there will be waves of terrible sadness, 20
which last sometimes for days; and dissatisfaction
with one's self, and irritation at others, and anger
at circumstances and stony insensibility, etc. etc.,
which taken together form a melancholy. Now,
painful as it is, this is sent to us for an enlighten- 25
ment. It always passes off, and we learn about
life from it, and we ought to learn a great many
good things if we react on it rightly. (From margin.) (For instance, you learn how good a thing

your home is, and your country, and your brothers,
and you may learn to be more considerate of other
people, who, you now learn, may have their inner
weaknesses and sufferings, too.)   Many persons
5 take a kind of sickly delight in hugging it; and some
sentimental ones may even be proud of it, as showing a fine sorrowful kind of sensibility. Such
persons make a regular habit of the luxury of woe.
That is the worst possible reaction on it.   It is
10 usually a sort of disease, when we get it strong,
arising from the organism, having generated some
poison in the blood; and we mustn't submit to it
an hour longer than we can help, but jump at
every chance to attend to anything cheerful or
15 comic or take part in anything active that will
divert us from our mean, pining inward state of
being.   When it passes off, as I said, we know more
than we did before.   And we must try to make it
last as short a time as possible.   The worst of it
20 often is that, while we are in it, we don't *want* to
get out of it.   We hate it, and yet we prefer staying
in it — that is a part of the disease.   If we find
ourselves like that, we must make ourselves do
something different, go with people, speak cheer-
25 fully, set ourselves to some hard work, make ourselves sweat, etc.; and that is the good way of
reacting that makes of us a valuable character.
The disease makes you think of *yourself* all the time;
and the way out of it is to keep as busy as we can

thinking of *things* and of *other people* — no matter
what's the matter with ourself.

I have no doubt you are doing as well as you
know how, darling little Peg; but we have to learn
everything, and I also have no doubt that you'll 5
manage it better and better if you ever have any
more of it, and soon it will fade away, simply leaving you with more experience. The great thing
for you *now*, I should suppose, would be to enter as
friendly as possible into the interest of the Clarke 10
children. If you like them, or acted as if you liked
them, you needn't trouble about the question of
whether they like you or not. They probably will,
fast enough; and if they don't, it will be their funeral, not yours. But this is a great lecture; so I will 15
stop. The great thing about it is that it is all true.

The baths are threatening to disagree with me
again; so I may stop them soon. Will let you
know as quick as anything is decided. Good news
from home: the Merrimans have taken the Irving 20
Street house for another year, and the Wambaughs
(of the Law School) have taken Chocorua, though at
a reduced rent. The weather here is almost con-
tinuously cold and sunless. Your mother is sleeping, and will doubtless add a word to this when she 25
wakes. Keep a merry heart — "time and the hour
run through the roughest day" — and believe me
ever your most loving

W. J.

TO JOHN D. JOHNSTON

Abraham Lincoln

January 2, 1851

DEAR JOHNSTON:

Your request for eighty dollars I do not think
it best to comply with now. At the various times
5 when I have helped you a little you have said to me,
"We can get along very well now"; but in a very
short time I find you in the same difficulty again.
Now, this can only happen by some defect in your
conduct. What that defect is, I think I know.
10 You are not lazy, and still you are an idler. I
doubt whether, since I saw you, you have done a
good whole day's work in any one day. You do
not very much dislike to work, and still you do not
work much, merely because it does not seem to
15 you that you could get much for it. This habit of
uselessly wasting time is the whole difficulty; it is
vastly important to you, and still more so to your
children, that you should break the habit. It is
more important to them, because they have longer
20 to live, and can keep out of an idle habit before

they are in it, easier than they can get out after
they are in.

You are now in need of some money; and what
I propose is that you shall go to work, "tooth and
nail," for somebody who will give you money for it. 5
Let father and your boys take charge of your things
at home, prepare for a crop, and make a crop, and
you go to work for the best money wages, or in
discharge of any debt you owe, that you can get;
and, to secure you a fair reward for your labor, 10
I now promise you that for every dollar you will,
between this and the first of May, get for your own
labor, either in money or as your own indebtedness,
I will then give you one other dollar.   By this, if
you hire yourself at ten dollars a month, from me 15
you will get ten more, making twenty dollars a
month for your work.   In this I do not mean that
you shall go off to St. Louis, or the lead mines, or
the gold mines in California, but I mean for you
to go at it for the best wages you can get close 20
to home in Coles County.

Now, if you will do this, you will be soon out of
debt, and, what is better, you will have a habit that
will keep you from getting in debt again.   But, if
I should now clear you out of debt, next year you 25
would be just as deep in as ever.   You say you
would almost give your place in heaven for seventy
or eighty dollars.   Then you value your place in
heaven very cheap, for I am sure you can, with the

offer I make, get the seventy or eighty dollars for four or five months' work. You say if I will furnish you the money you will deed me the land, and if you don't pay the money back you will deliver posses-
5 sion. Nonsense! If you can't live now with the land, how will you then live without it? You have always been very kind to me, and I do not mean to be unkind to you. On the contrary, if you will but follow my advice, you will find it worth more
10 than eighty times eighty dollars to you.

Affectionately your brother,
A. Lincoln

TO HIS SON

Charles Dickens

MY DEAREST PLORN,

I write this note to-day because your going away
is much upon my mind, and because I want you to
have a few parting words from me to think of now
and then at quiet times.   I need not tell you that I 5
love you dearly, and am very, very sorry in my
heart to part with you.   But this life is half made
up of partings, and these pains must be borne.   It is
my comfort and my sincere conviction that you are
going to try the life for which you are best fitted. 10
I think its freedom and wildness more suited to you
than any experiment in a study or office would ever
have been; and without that training, you could
have followed no other suitable occupation.

What you have always wanted until now has 15
been a set, steady, constant purpose.   I therefore
exhort you to persevere in a thorough determination
to do whatever you have to do as well as you can
do it.   I was not so old as you are now when I first
had to win my food, and do this out of this deter- 20
mination, and I have never slackened in it since.

Never take a mean advantage of any one in any

transaction, and never be hard upon people who are in your power. Try to do to others as you would have them do to you, and do not be discouraged if they fail sometimes. It is much better for you that they should fail in obeying the greatest rule laid down by our Savior than that you should.

I put a New Testament among your books, for the very same reasons, and with the very same hopes that made me write an easy account of it for you, when you were a little child; because it is the best book that ever was or will be known in the world, and because it teaches you the best lessons by which any human creature who tries to be truthful and faithful to duty can possibly be guided. As your brothers have gone away, one by one, I have written to each such words as I am now writing you, and have entreated them all to guide themselves by this book, putting aside the interpretations and inventions of men.

You will remember that you have never at home been wearied about religious observances or mere formalities. I have always been anxious not to weary my children with such things before they are old enough to form opinions respecting them. You will therefore understand the better that I now most solemnly impress upon you the truth and beauty of the Christian religion, as it came from Christ himself, and the impossibility of your going far wrong if you humbly but heartily respect it.

Charles Dickens to His Son

Only one thing more on this head. The more we are in earnest as to feeling it, the less we are disposed to hold forth about it. Never abandon the wholesome practice of saying your own private prayers, night and morning. I have never aban-5 doned it myself, and I know the comfort of it.

I hope you will always be able to say in after life that you had a kind father.   You cannot show your affection for him so well, or make him so happy, as by doing your duty.   10

Your affectionate father,
Charles Dickens

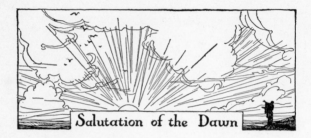

Salutation of the Dawn

LISTEN to the exhortation of the dawn.
Look to this day!
For it is life,
The very life of life.
In its brief course lie all the varieties
And realities of your existence;
The bliss of growth,
The glory of action,
The splendor of beauty.
For yesterday is a dream
And to-morrow is only a vision.
But to-day well lived
Makes every yesterday a dream of happiness
And every to-morrow a vision of hope.
Look well, therefore, to this day!
Such is the salutation of the dawn.

— From the Sanskrit

APPENDIX

APPENDIX

THE MAGIC SPEAR

An old Hebraic tradition, used by Milton in *Paradise Lost*, represents Ithuriel, the angel formed of fire, encompassed by light, and carrying a magic spear, as a heavenly messenger from God to man. He is heard and seen only by the one whom the message concerns. In *Paradise Lost*, Ithuriel, sent into the Garden of Eden to find Satan, discovers him disguised as a toad crouched at the ear of Eve. Touched by the revealing spear, the fallen angel stands forth in his true guise.

RUDYARD KIPLING

The Hour of the Angel, Kipling's poetic version of the old tradition, sounds the keynote of this book. Here are some of the glorious company who met the test successfully when they unflinchingly faced the hour which

> Will spring on us, for the first time, the test
> Of our sole unbacked competence and power
> Up to the limit of our years and dower
> Of judgment — or beyond.

Appendix

In the blinding antarctic blizzard, when that revealing spear touches Scott and his brave companions, they stand forth as men of heroic mold, facing their tragic fate with that fine courage which every "act, habit, thought, and passion" had bred in them.

The icy peril of the sea is the form in which the passengers and crew of the ill-fated *Titanic* and the *Lusitania* see Ithuriel's spear approach. And Commander Rodgers, Commander Byrd, Amundsen, Ellsworth, flying over land and sea to widen our knowledge of the earth and sky, face the Angel's Hour many times. The brave aviators carrying the air mail must measure up to the exacting task.

Roosevelt makes himself fit, overcomes ill health, finds relaxation in strenuous effort, accomplishes more than some men would in five lifetimes. In the story of the Alamo, he shows us Crockett and the type of men that helped to conquer the western wilderness and to push forward the frontier. We see cheerful endurance, poise in the face of peril, service, and the toil which the pioneers ungrudgingly bore. And Anna Shaw shows the pioneer child faced with dangers and responsibilities before which we might, to-day, cringe and shrink. Have we still the pioneer virtues? We may, at least, prepare to meet the present-day problems of the home, the school, and the community, where initiative, courage, coöperation, service, and devotion to duty are needed to-day just as much as in the pioneer days.

Livingstone, greatest of explorers, opens up a vast continent and faces the angel's spear thrust with sub-

The Magic Spear

lime calm. Later, we see Gorgas, the devoted scientist, driving devastating disease before him in many lands, finishing his life's work in the great continent explored by Livingstone.

Grenfell, the missionary doctor, finds that "the joys of life lie in us, not in things." On the bleak Labrador coast he searches for opportunity to fulfill his beautiful idea that "the good Samaritan went across the road because he wanted to."

Clara Barton not only brings aid to the soldier on the battlefield but helps to enlarge the Red Cross to a world-wide service which knows not creed, nor race, nor nationality.

Michael Pupin on the Serbian hills sees in the stars and the fields the great forces of nature, and fares forth, guided by his unselfish mother, to a new land where he successfully meets the test of character. Many mothers have been the guiding forces which kept their boys and girls steady in crises. And he finds that faith in God does not conflict with scientific curiosity but is helped by it.

Cheerful Mary White brings happiness wherever she moves. Cheerful everyday living is often harder to achieve than a sensational deed. The angel's spear may touch us in the kitchen or in the shop, in the schoolroom or behind the counter, as well as in the wide spaces of earth, air, or sea.

Huxley, James, Wilson are great philosophers and teachers who show us the guideposts which, if followed, will develop a right attitude toward life, toward our neighbors, toward other nations. We must play the

297

game, and we must learn the rules in order that our play shall be not aimless nor profitless, but worth while. Some one has said, "Football is often like life; one fellow carries the ball and gets most of the credit. Yet ten men have helped him to push through and without them he would not have gained an inch." The conditions of modern life require us to learn how to coöperate.

Peg's wise father, William James, steers her away from a weakness which would disable her before the angel's thrust; Dickens shows his son some ways in which he may make himself fit; Lincoln's stepbrother fails to measure up and becomes a shiftless ne'er-do-well.

In reading fictitious lives, we may live through vicarious experiences which will often help us when we are faced by similar circumstances. The sailors who brave the seas, like White Jacket, in order that we may be more comfortable on land or travel safely by sea; the boy, like Richard, who owns to wrongdoing, and the country lad who shows a mistaken loyalty to Richard; little Glory Goldie giving her fish to the old man; Bruce Landon returning the fish to the rightful owner; Giles Meiklejohn struggling, like Strickland, with conscience, facing the angel's thrust: all face problems that test their "dower of judgment."

In the stories of Three Eyes and the fire-dog, we see that courage and loyalty are often shown by animals as well as by human beings. The helpfulness, coöperation, dependability, and initiative shown by Putnam are among the traits which endear animals to us and call for kindly treatment in return for the services they render us. Read the long honor roll of carrier pigeons, camels, mules, dogs, and horses lost in the Great Waı in the line of duty. No shirkers were they.

Wholesome recreation is one of the best guides to fitness. In the word *recreation* you may find its real meaning — that which re-creates or makes new. Reading good books, gardening, collecting mineral specimens or moths or butterflies are all good and valuable forms of recreation. Travel afoot and explore the unknown streets of your town; discover for yourself the wide-spreading landscape of the country about you; learn the joy of looking above at the billowy white clouds, or below at the grass or the varied forms of animation on the road; learn to hear music in the breeze and to see gorgeous beauty in the reds and yellows of the sunset, the soft grays of autumn, and the fairylike greens of spring.

Some years ago, in the old walled city of Manila, a long religious procession carrying tall candles was passing through the narrow streets. Suddenly the tropic night fell; the blackness was pierced only by the brilliant stars above, among which shone resplendent the beautiful Southern Cross. As the leader entered the votive church which was the goal of the procession, he lighted his candle at the altar; then, coming out, he passed the flame to those nearest him, the light quickly flashing from hand to hand, illuminating the dark streets and making a long path of light.

So do poets and narrators of fine thoughts and doers of noble deeds pass along the inspiring thought or word or deed or life, making a trail of light down the centuries to guide uncertain feet along the hazardous road of life.

Appendix

Silver Wings

Raoul Fauconnier Whitfield was born in New York City. He was an ace in the World War, having received his training in San Antonio, Texas; the war gave him the opportunity of flying over the greater part of France and England. On his return to America, Mr. Whitfield did various kinds of work on the Pittsburgh *Post*, reporting, reviewing plays, and editing a humorous column. He now devotes all his time to the writing of fiction, utilizing his experiences as an aviator for "copy." His winter home is in Pasadena, California, where he enjoys his dogs, his books, and his airplane.

1. Mr. Whitfield says: "Drama — the sharply, intensely dramatic second or seconds — I love. And there is drama in the sky, in the cockpits of a plane. Silent drama, quite often — but drama just the same." What is the most dramatic moment in *Silver Wings*?

2. What incident in the story seems most sportsmanlike?

3. What incident seems most unsportsmanlike?

4. Interpret the meaning of the story in the light of Kipling's poem, *The Hour of the Angel*.

5. What points of resemblance do you find between *Silver Wings* and *The Riverman*?

6. Read the last paragraph. What is the colonel's meaning?

7. Make a list of the words in the story that are peculiar to aviation. Give their meaning.

8. Read aloud what you think is the best descriptive passage in the story.

Notes, Questions, and Topics for Study

Lindbergh Flies Alone

Colonel Charles Lindbergh studied at the University of Wisconsin, mastered the theory and practice of aviation, and later became an air-mail pilot. The editorial refers to his lone flight across the Atlantic Ocean, May 20, 1927, to Paris.

CHARLES LINDBERGH · *International Newsreel*

1. What qualities enabled Colonel Lindbergh to accomplish his feat?

2. What connection do you see between his arduous work as a mail pilot and his flight across the Atlantic Ocean?

3. What quality did Colonel Lindbergh reveal when he referred to his airplane and himself as *we?*

4. Read his book, *We*, and make an oral report on it to the class.

5. Read Nancy Byrd Turner's poem, *The Ballad of*

Appendix

Lindbergh the Lucky, aloud to the class. Interpret the poem.

6. Memorize the editorial from the *Sun*.

7. What experience of Colonel Lindbergh's served as Ithuriel's magic spear?

Lost and Found

Octavus Roy Cohen was born in Charleston, South Carolina, in 1891. He was graduated from Porter Military Academy and Clemson College. He has been associated with the editorial departments of various newspapers, in the North and the South. His fame rests chiefly on a series of stories about negro life, contributed to the *Saturday Evening Post*. Mr. Cohen makes his home in Birmingham, Alabama.

1. Find the sentences and phrases that reveal the chief difference between the young man and the girl in *Lost and Found*.

2. Explain the appropriateness of the title.

3. Interpret the meaning of the story in the light of Kipling's *The Hour of the Angel*.

4. How does the young man meet the test? How does the girl?

5. Can you cite any instances in real life or in literature of people who were subjected to severe tests? Did they stand the tests or not?

The Riverman

The wide outdoors, forests, lumber camps, and the smell of the pines and of the camp fire are associated in our minds with the name of Stewart Edward White.

Notes, Questions, and Topics for Study

Perhaps in his own Michigan forests — for he was born in Grand Rapids, in 1873 — he discovered the background and the material for many of his vivid tales. This story is found in a volume called *Blazed Trail Stories*. Other interesting books he has written are *Arizona Nights, African Camp Fires, The Blazed Trail,* and *Daniel Boone: Wilderness Scout*.

1. Who are the two chief characters in the story? Describe each briefly.

2. What is your definition of true sportsmanship?

3. What instance do you find in the story of a lack of sportsmanship?

4. What kind of man was Harry Thorpe?

5. Do you think that Jimmy Powers is speaking seriously in the last paragraph?

6. If he means literally what he says, wnat do you think of his motive in saving the life of Darrell?

7. What connection can you discover between this story and *The Hour of the Angel?*

8. List as many books as you can find on the subject of lumbering.

9. You would enjoy reading *Daniel Boone: Wilderness Scout* by Stewart Edward White.

Fishing on the Wrong Side

After achieving a reputation as a novelist and story-writer of delightful charm, Thomas Nelson Page (1853–1922) was appointed, in 1913, American ambassador to Italy.

His stories and novels exhale the charm of the Old Dominion, where Mr. Page was born and lived — at

Appendix

Oakland Plantation, Hanover County, Virginia. The chapter included in this text is taken from a novel called *On Newfound River*. A stranger, Doctor Browne, has incurred the hatred of Major Landon by purchasing some property formerly belonging to the older Landons, which the major desired to get back into the hands of the Landons. Major Landon forbids Bruce, his son, to go over on the Browne side of the river. Bruce disobeys, taking Dick, a colored boy, with him. As the story develops, Doctor Browne turns out to be the major's long-lost brother. The story ends happily.

Harris & Ewing

THOMAS NELSON PAGE

1. Read the selection, *Richard Confesses*, and compare Bruce and Richard. What was the offense of each? How was each made to see the error of his ways?

2. What is Bruce's chief defect of character?

3. Read Pupin's description of his mother in *My Childhood*. Compare and contrast her with Bruce's mother.

4. Quote proverbs about a hot temper.

5. Suppose Bruce had not agreed to return the fish. What effect would such a decision have had on his character?

Notes, Questions, and Topics for Study

Fishing

In *Mårbacka* the Swedish author, Selma Lagerlöf (1858–   ), in most interesting fashion, tells the story of her childhood. She was a delicate child of great mental activity. She became a strong woman, however, and a writer of great power and distinction. *The Story of Gösta Berling, Herr Arne's Hoard*, and *The*

SELMA LAGERLÖF IN HER LIBRARY AT MÅRBACKA

Wonderful Adventures of Nils are some of her books. This selection is taken from her story called *The Emperor of Portugallia*.

1. Did the old man do right in taking Glory Goldie's fish? Does necessity excuse wrongdoing? Discuss this question.

2. What element in Glory Goldie's last offer to the old man induced him to accept it?

3. When Glory Goldie looked herself squarely in the face, she saw selfishness. How did she show that the angel's spear had touched her and that she had successfully met the test?

The Finger of God

Percival Wilde was born in New York City in 1887. For five years after his graduation from Columbia University he was connected with the banking business. Then he became a reviewer for the New York *Times* and the New York *Post*. Later he turned his attention to play-writing. During the World War he served as ensign in the United States navy, acquiring a good deal of experience which he utilized in one-act plays. In addition to stories and plays he wrote *The Craftsmanship of the One-Act Play*, an excellent discussion of the subject.

1. How and when does Strickland meet the Angel's Hour?
2. Who in this play represents Ithuriel?
3. Another of Percival Wilde's plays has honesty for its subject. In *Confessional*, Baldwin, who has the reputation of being honest, is guilty of moral failure. Read the play, and contrast Strickland and Baldwin.

The Brown Wallet

Stacy Aumonier (1887–1928), the author of many interesting stories, began as a decorative designer and landscape painter. Then he became a society entertainer, giving recitals of his own character sketches. In 1913 he began writing for the magazines of both Eng-

Notes, Questions, and Topics for Study

land and America. During the World War, Aumonier served as a private in the British army, being assigned, later, to the department of map-making. He lived at St. John's Wood, London.

1. How had Giles Meiklejohn's father failed in his duty to his son?

2. Who is the better parent: the indulgent one who allows his children too much spending money and too much play, and neglects to train them to endure hardily, enjoy interesting work, and make right choices; or the parent like Pupin's mother, or Captain Scott, or Roosevelt?

3. Why should one plan one's future? How could Giles have escaped all this misery had his life been planned?

4. "Experience is a hard teacher." What does this mean?

5. Did Eleanor meet successfully the Angel's Hour? Explain.

6. How does wrongdoing enslave one? Explain in Giles's case. Why is right choosing important?

Richard Confesses

George Meredith (1828–1909), born at Portsmouth, England, wrote great novels and great poetry. Besides *The Ordeal of Richard Feverel* some of his greatest books are *Diana of the Crossways*, *The Egoist*, and *Rhoda Fleming*. His enormous vocabulary is often difficult for the average reader to grasp. At his home, Box Hill, many other great writers, as Hardy, Shaw, and Barrie, used to visit him. His ashes were buried in the little

Appendix

cemetery of the village of Dorking, near which he lived.

In *The Ordeal of Richard Feverel* George Meredith tells the story of a father and his son, Sir Austin Feverel and his son Richard. Richard, with a chum, Ripton Thompson, celebrates his fourteenth birthday by poaching on Farmer Blaize's property, shooting a cock pheas-

GEORGE MEREDITH

ant. Farmer Blaize uses his horsewhip on the boys when he discovers and catches them. In revenge Richard bribes Tom Bakewell, a country lout, to fire Farmer Blaize's rick. Tom is caught and clapped into jail. The chapter here shows that Richard's conscience is pricking him.

1. How did Richard meet the Angel's Hour?

2. Why was it cowardly in Richard to incite a poor ignorant fellow to fire the rick? What do you think of a person who leads a weaker one into wrongdoing?

3. What do you think of Richard's attitude toward Farmer Blaize? Did Richard deserve his punishment?

4. Have we any right to damage other people's property even though we are willing to pay for the damage?

5. Do you know of instances where a confession of wrongdoing indicated a brave and noble disposition? If so, give the class an account of the instance.

308

Notes, Questions, and Topics for Study

Cape Horn

Herman Melville (1819–1891), author of famous stories of the sea and the South Sea islands, was born in New York City. His paternal grandfather was a prominent patriot and is said to have been the last American to wear the cocked hat, wearing it until his death in 1832. Melville's maternal grandfather fought in the American army at Quebec, later becoming commandant of Fort George and also of Fort Schuyler.

HERMAN MELVILLE

Herman Melville, under the pen name of "White Jacket," tells, in the book of that title, his own experiences as a sailor on an American frigate, supposed to be the famous *Constitution*. The narrative begins at the frigate's last harbor in the Pacific, in 1843, and tells the story of the homeward voyage, giving interesting views of life on a man-of-war of that time.

In *Typee* Melville tells the story of his capture by savages on one of the Marquesas Islands, from which he was rescued, finally, by an Australian whaler. *Moby Dick* is a fine whaling story.

The selection in this text is a chapter from *White Jacket*.

Appendix

1. Cape Horn proved the mettle of White Jacket. How?

2. Did Captain Claret know how to play the game well?

3. Why was Mad Jack not disciplined for disobedience?

4. Persons in authority should have superior ability, knowledge, and character. Why? Why should ships' officers have poise, cheerfulness, knowledge, a sense of responsibility, and self-control? Do you know of other occupations which require all these qualities for success? Tell of some recent incident in which one person's judgment saved many others.

5. What does Melville mean by saying we all should prepare for Cape Horn?

6. Success or failure depends largely on personality. Think of the successful people you know. What qualities have made these persons successful?

Three Eyes

Wilfred Grenfell, the missionary doctor of Labrador, was born February 28, 1865, near Chester, England. At fourteen, he won a scholarship in Marl-borough College, where self-government was successfully exercised by the pupils. Good form, among the boys of the school, included a nice attention to their personal appearance, which was especially shown at Sunday morning chapel, when each boy wore a flower in his buttonhole. Long after, Dr. Grenfell related how his mother used to send him a box of flowers every week, and he commented on this motherly thoughtfulness thus: "It is these deeds of love that never fade from the soul and to the last make their appeal to the wandering boy to 'arise' and do things."

His parents encouraged him to take an interest in natural objects and to collect mineral specimens, moths, butterflies, seaweed, shells, and abandoned birds' nests.

Harris & Ewing

WILFRED GRENFELL

After graduating from the London Hospital and University, the young doctor decided to devote his life to the service of the deep-sea sailors and fishermen. At first he worked among the men on the fishing boats of the North Sea; later he decided to answer the call from an even more necessitous field, the bleak Labrador coast. Hospital stations, schools, and social-service organization are visible evidences of Dr. Grenfell's long and devoted service on this inhospitable coast.

"Pitiable, indeed, would be the condition of the poor folk on the Labrador were it not for Dr. Grenfell and his brave coworkers of the Deep Sea Mission. For hundreds of miles along the coast they travel on their errands of mercy, braving the violent storms of the arctic winter, sleeping in the meanest huts, and risking their lives in open boats on the raging sea. Many are the lives they save."

This story of a dog's devotion is related by Dr. Grenfell in *Tales of the Labrador*. In *A Labrador Doctor* you may read Dr. Grenfell's stirring story of service to humanity.

1. Comment on these two statements by Doctor Grenfell: "The joys of life lie in us, not in things." "I have always believed that the good Samaritan went across the road because he wanted to." Who was the good Samaritan?

2. What fine traits did this dog Three Eyes exhibit?

3. Why are dogs necessary to the Labrador folk? What service have they rendered in arctic exploration? What lessons can they teach us?

4. There are many famous dogs: Ulysses' faithful hound; Scott's Maida; Byron's Boatswain; Rip Van Winkle's dog; Greyfriars Bobby. Narrate some story you may know of a dog, cat, horse, or other animal that helped mankind and showed fine traits of character.

Bruce: A Fire-Dog of New York

Sarah Noble Ives was born at Grosse Ile, Michigan, and educated in Port Huron, Detroit, New York, and Paris. She lives in New York City, where she pursues her profession of landscape painter, illustrator, and contributor to magazines and newspapers.

The selection in this text is taken from *Dog Heroes of Many Lands*.

1. How did Bruce's sheep-herding instinct help him?

2. Have you read any other story in this text in which early experiences were later of great service?

Notes, Questions, and Topics for Study

3. Compare Three Eyes and Bruce. Give instances of their seeming ability to reason.

4. What qualities of character do the owners of Three Eyes and Bruce exhibit?

5. In Central Park, in New York City, there is a monument to Balto, the Siberian dog that went on an errand of mercy. Find out the facts about him and tell the story to your class.

Putnam: A Horse

The seizure, by various European and Asiatic powers, of large areas of Chinese territory resulted, in 1900, in a series of outrages upon foreigners perpetrated by a sect called "Boxers," or the "Fists of Righteous Harmony." "China for the Chinese" was the idea which impelled them to kill foreigners and to besiege the foreign ministers in the legation quarter of Peking.

An international army marched from the coast to the Chinese capital; August 14, 1900, they stormed the wall around the city, Americans and Japanese leading the attack. Captain Reilly, of the Fifth Field Artillery, was killed with other Americans. The next day the troops entered the Forbidden City, which white men had rarely seen, much less entered. The empress and her court fled; after centuries of uninterrupted national existence, the Celestial Empire soon came to an end.

The slope up which Putnam dragged the gun and the other horses was about two miles from Peking and commanded the great gate and the huge guardhouse on the Tartar Wall around the city. The account of the incident is a true story.

Appendix

1. Animals often inspire courage in human beings. How did Putnam inspire the soldiers?

2. Name some of the famous horses in history and literature, and give an account of each.

3. Putnam's team-mates in the battery failed to coöperate with him; so he had to drag them as well as the gun. What part does coöperation play in a successful enterprise?

ANNA HOWARD SHAW

A Pioneer Girl

The romantic life story of the author, lecturer, and suffragette, Anna Howard Shaw (1847–1919), is vividly told in *The Story of a Pioneer*, from which the selection in this text is taken. Born in Newcastle-on-Tyne, England, Anna was but four years old when the family emigrated to the United States, settling first at New Bedford, Massachusetts, and later going out as pioneers to the Michigan woods. The pioneer girl learned to use a saw and hatchet and helped not only to build their wilderness home but also to make the rude furniture needed; with her brother's help she dug a well. While her father and brother served in the Union army, Anna was the main support of the family.

314

She taught school; as there were few books, one pupil used a hymn book, others an almanac, as readers. Her study for the ministry and her ardent work for the woman-suffrage movement were but a part of her varied activities in later life.

DR. SHAW'S EARLY MICHIGAN HOME

1. What fine qualities of character did Anna Shaw, the pioneer girl, have?

2. How do you think she acquired the power to face calmly the experiences related in the selection?

3. Can you mention other girls or boys, or men and women, who showed self-control in a crisis?

4. Name the pioneer virtues.

5. What present-day situations call for pioneer virtues?

6. Read Hamlin Garland's *Boy Life on the Prairie*, another story of pioneer life in the Middle West.

7. Hospitality was an unwritten law of the frontier. Why?

Clara Barton

The story of the American Red Cross may be read in the history of the Red Cross written by Clara Barton (1821–1912) and published by the United States government. Not only in the Great War, but in time of famine in Russia and in China, of earthquakes in Japan, and of floods in China and the Mississippi Valley, the American

Red Cross has shown an international sympathy which is limited by neither race nor creed. The Junior Red Cross, connected with the older society, accomplishes much in establishing friendly relations among the nations.

1. How did Clara Barton's childhood prepare her for a life of usefulness?

2. Make a brief report on the life of Florence Nightingale.

Wide World Photos

CLARA BARTON

3. Make a report on the work of your local chapter of the Red Cross.

The Last Letters of Captain Scott

Captain Robert Falcon Scott, who had led an earlier antarctic expedition in the *Discovery*, sailed from Cardiff, Wales, in the *Terra Nova*, June 15, 1910, to discover the south pole.

After enduring fearful hardships and suffering the loss of his ponies, Scott, with four companions, reached the south pole on January 17, 1911, only to find that Amundsen, the Norwegian explorer, had, just a month before, achieved the honor of discovering the long-sought goal.

Notes, Questions, and Topics for Study

The little party of five, frost-bitten, ill, weary, began the strenuous 800-mile hike, over icy mountains, terrifying crevasses, and dangerous glaciers, back to their base. The angry antarctic blizzard seized the devoted men with icy and relentless fury. One was lost on the terrible Boardmore Glacier; another walked to his death in the blizzard. Scott, with Lieutenant Bowers and Dr. Wilson, was the last to die. In a wind-swept tent on that antarctic waste ended one of the most heroic epics in the long and tragic tale of polar exploration. Some months later a rescuing party found the three bodies with Scott's diary and letters.

ROBERT FALCON SCOTT

Sir James Matthew Barrie, the Scottish writer, read the last letter Captain Scott wrote him to the students of St. Andrew's University, in Edinburgh. At the close he said: "I think it may uplift you all to stand for a moment by that tent and listen, as he says, to their songs and cheery conversation. How comely a thing is affliction borne cheerfully, which is not beyond the reach of the humblest of us! What is beauty? It is these hard-bitten men singing courage to you from their tent; it is the waves of their island home crooning of their deeds to you who are to follow them."

Appendix

1. Barrie says Scott made himself fit as a lad. In what ways did Scott make himself fit?

2. How and where did Captain Scott meet the test of character, the Angel's Hour?

3. What fine qualities besides courage do Scott's life and letters exhibit? What splendid traits did the five men all show?

Keystone View Co.

JAMES MATTHEW BARRIE

4. How did Scott and his companions exhibit true sportsmanship?

5. Give some examples of men and women who met defeat bravely and cheerfully.

6. Cite instances of men and women who met success humbly and modestly.

7. Discuss this topic: "Can One Be a Successful Failure?"

William Crawford Gorgas

Born in Alabama, William C. Gorgas (1854–1920) studied medicine and surgery at Bellevue Medical College, New York City. He became a surgeon in the United States army and, in 1898, chief sanitary officer of Havana.

At one time yellow fever was a scourge in the southern states, the West Indies, and adjacent lands. The French, because of the heavy loss of life, had abandoned

318

the building of the Panama Canal. Thousands of people died of the plague.

Dr. James Carroll, Dr. Walter Reed, Dr. Jesse Lazear, and Dr. Aristides Agramonte were associated with Gorgas in cleaning up Havana. They proved that yellow fever was carried by mosquitoes. By destroying these insect pests they stamped out the disease. Later, when the United States built the Panama Canal, the work was made possible only by the eradication of this terrible scourge of the tropics. Later still, in South America and in South Africa, large areas were made safe for white men by the application of the sanitary discoveries made by Gorgas and his

Underwood & Underwood

WILLIAM C. GORGAS

associates, some of whom lost their lives in pursuing their scientific researches.

1. Dr. Gorgas greatly admired Livingstone. What traits did both have in common?

2. Make brief reports to the class on Louis Pasteur, Edward Jenner, Edward L. Trudeau, Walter Reed, Hideyo Noguchi, and John R. Kissenger.

3. What is the Hippocratic oath? Read it to the class.

4. Read Ian Maclaren's story, *A Doctor of the Old School*.

Appendix

5. How can you help to make your city, your town, your village, and the premises of your house a better place in which to live?

Mary White

In the article on page 211, written by William Allen White (1868–), the father of Mary White, one may easily discover the skilled journalist who, as editor and proprietor of the daily and weekly Emporia *Gazette*, has made Kansas and Emporia famous. Born in Emporia, Mr. White is a typical American. *The Court of Boyville*, *In Our Town*, *God's Puppets*, and *The Martial Adventures of Henry and Me* are the titles of some of his books.

Harris & Ewing
MICHAEL I. PUPIN

1. What were Mary White's chief characteristics?

2. What was the secret of her happiness?

3. Comment on Mary White's taste in reading.

4. How does the author make his article especially readable?

My Childhood

Michael I. Pupin (1858–), now professor of electromechanics at Columbia University, in his interesting autobiography *From Immigrant to Inventor*, tells the

320

Notes, Questions, and Topics for Study

story of his life. Born in Banat, which was then part of Hungary, he came to this country as a lad, achieving, by his own efforts, an enviable success as physicist and inventor. The selection is taken from *From Immigrant to Inventor*.

1. How did Michael Pupin's mother influence him?

2. Name other mothers who exerted a great influence on their sons.

3. What lessons did Pupin learn from the open life in the field?

4. How did Pupin's experiences with light and sound affect his future career?

5. Read other chapters in *From Immigrant to Inventor* and report on them to your class.

SAM HOUSTON

Remember the Alamo

David Crockett, a native of Tennessee, was born in 1786, and became famous as a pioneer hunter and politician. During his three terms in Congress he achieved a reputation as an eccentric humorist, whose oratory was distinguished alike for hard sense and rugged English.

Crockett died fighting for the new republic of Texas, which, under the Lone Star, maintained its independence until it became one of the United States in 1845.

Appendix

The story of the Alamo is told by Roosevelt in his *Stories of the West*.

1. Tell, in your own words, the story of the Alamo.
2. How did Crockett's death help to free Texas?
3. Name others besides Gorgas and Crockett who, by sacrifice, helped others to a more comfortable living.
4. What qualities did Crockett have which Roosevelt also had? Cite some ways in which school boys and girls can show patriotism and good citizenship.
5. Scouts and pioneers blaze the trail for others and give us lessons in patience, courage, and unselfishness. Name some scouts and pioneers who blazed trails in your state.

Underwood & Underwood

THEODORE ROOSEVELT

The Roosevelt Spirit Is Not Dead

Theodore Roosevelt, twenty-sixth and youngest president of the United States, was born in New York City, October 27, 1858. He was of Dutch ancestry on his father's side. His grandfather explored the Ohio and the Mississippi on the first steamboat that navigated these waters. Roosevelt's mother was descended from Archibald Bullock, an early governor of Georgia.

After graduating from Harvard, Roosevelt served in the New York State Assembly. In 1884 he went west to a Dakota ranch to recover his health. His love of the outdoors and of pioneer life stimulated his interest in the early history of our country, and resulted in many books bearing on the development of the United States.

He served as police commissioner of New York City; served on the national Civil Service Commission; was assistant secretary of the navy, colonel of the "Rough Riders" in Cuba, governor of New York in 1898, and vice president of the United States in 1900, becoming president in 1901 on McKinley's assassination; and was elected president in 1904.

On many hunting and exploring trips to the western country, to Africa, and to South America, he found wide opportunity to gratify his love of nature and to revel in the naturalist's life. These varied activities were ended only by his death at Oyster Bay, New York, January 6, 1919.

In his letters to his children and in this well-written article by the distinguished journalist and author, Julian Street (1879–   ), we see vivid sketches of the naturalist president, and catch charming glimpses of the father with his children. We see, too, the joy he found in surmounting difficulties.

1. What did Theodore Roosevelt try to train his children to do? How did he train them?

2. What qualities are needed to overcome obstacles? Which Roosevelt trait do you admire most? Why?

3. Roosevelt was a good citizen and a good sportsman. What qualities are involved in these terms?

4. How can school boys and girls show a helpful

Appendix

initiative, good sportsmanship, self-reliance, and self-control?

I Meet a Lion

David Livingstone was born March 19, 1813, in Lanark, Scotland. From the age of ten he maintained himself, working in a cotton mill and saving his pennies

Ewing Galloway

DAVID LIVINGSTONE

to buy books. Working from six in the morning until eight at night, he acquired an education by studying at night, and, as he tells, by "placing the book on a portion of the spinning-jenny, so that I could catch sentence after sentence as I passed at my work."

At nineteen he became a spinner, and was able to earn enough to attend medical and Greek classes and divinity lectures at Glasgow University. "Looking back over this period of toil, I cannot but feel thankful that it formed such a material part of my education; and, were I to begin life again, I should like to pass through the same hardy training."

On completing his university courses, he sailed for Algoa Bay, Africa, December 8, 1840, as a medical missionary. Northward he traveled to the great regions marked on the map as "unexplored regions." Living with the natives, he learned their tongues. He made them his friends by treating them kindly, curing many of their sick, and trying to break up the slave trade. He also helped to open up trade routes, exploring Lakes Victoria, Nyassa, and Tanganyika and Victoria Falls, and found the sources of some of the great African rivers. His hardships during his thirty-three years as an explorer were relieved by several trips back to England, though at times he was lost, for years, to the outside world. In his diary we find, for October 24, 1871, this entry: "When my spirits were at their lowest ebb, the good Samaritan was close at hand; for one morning Susi came running at the top of his speed, and gasped out, 'An Englishman! I see him!' and off he darted to meet him. The American flag at the head of a caravan told of the nationality of the stranger. It was Henry M. Stanley, the traveling correspondent of the New York *Herald* sent by James Gordon Bennett, at an expense of more than £4000, to obtain accurate information about Dr. Livingstone if living, and, if dead, to bring home my bones. I really do feel extremely grateful and at the same time am a little ashamed at not being more worthy of the generosity." Stanley brought mail, supplies, and news which heartened the weary explorer.

Livingstone, urged by Stanley to come out with him, decided to stay and finish the great work he had begun. Their parting was an affecting scene. Stanley turned back now and then to look once more at the lonely figure of an old man in gray clothes, who, with slow step and bent head, was returning to his wilderness solitude. This was Livingstone's last look at a white man.

325

Appendix

About a year later, in the early morning, Susi, his faithful servant, found the doctor kneeling by the bed, his face in his hands. The explorer's work was done. Susi, with other devoted natives, carried the body with his diaries and other possessions, through miles and miles of forest, swamp, and hostile villages, to the coast. And these heroic blacks had recently been slaves.

From Zanzibar the body was borne by ship to England, where the last journey of the great explorer ended in the nave of Westminster Abbey. There he was entombed near England's sovereigns. He brought light into dark places and revealed a continent.

1. The life of Dr. Livingstone, largely spent with savages in tropical wildernesses, demanded certain noble traits. What were they?

2. How had Livingstone's boyhood training made him fit?

3. He was a pioneer in helping to abolish slavery in Africa and in being kind to native races. Name other great men or women who have helped to make the world a better place for all mankind.

4. What qualities must one have to be a great explorer like Stanley or Livingstone? Are any men, to-day, exhibiting such traits?

5. A sense of duty impelled Livingstone to stay at his post even when Stanley urged him to leave. A sense of duty impelled Mark Twain to write books and give lectures in order to pay the debts of the publishers to whom he felt a moral obligation. Sir Walter Scott, bankrupt, acted in similar fashion. Do you know of

Notes, Questions, and Topics for Study

other instances where a sense of loyalty or duty kept one at a laborious or uncongenial task?

How to Get the Best Out of Books

Richard Le Gallienne (1866–   ) is a critic, essayist, poet, and novelist. His graceful yet simple style is evident in this article taken from one of his volumes of essays.

Some other books by Le Gallienne are *George Meredith*, *Young Lives*, *Pieces of Eight*, and *The Junk Man and Other Poems*.

Though born in Liverpool, Le Gallienne has long lived in the United States.

1. Name a few books that you have recently read with pleasure.

2. Are there any books which you have read more than once? Give your reasons for liking them.

3. What books serve you as a playground where you may forget your cares?

4. Quote other writers on books and reading; for example, Francis Bacon and John Ruskin.

The Game of Life

Born in the little village of Ealing, near London, Thomas Henry Huxley (1825–1895) early showed an interest in science which led to extensive studies in the natural and physical sciences. His lectures to workingmen, expressed as they were in simple language, aroused a popular interest in the laws of nature and man's place in nature. His ideal was to be perfectly sincere in one's life and in one's work.

Appendix

The presidency of the famous Royal Society was bestowed on him in 1883 in recognition of his services to scientific study and research.

1. What is life compared to? Why should one learn the rules of the game?

2. How does Huxley define education?

THOMAS HENRY HUXLEY

3. Huxley classes knowledge under three heads: intellect, will, affections. Under which one would you place sympathy with your fellows; a knowledge of the laws of health; kindness to the unfortunate; obedience to parents and superiors; the ability to say "No" when necessary; the power to think straight; initiative; courage to surmount difficulties?

4. If you play the game of life well, what does Huxley say will be your reward?

The King's Jewel

Dr. Henry van Dyke (1852–   ), associated with Princeton University after his pastorate at the Brick Presbyterian Church, New York City, became United States minister to the Netherlands. He was born at Germantown, Pennsylvania, and lives at Princeton, New Jersey. He has written charming essays of out-

Notes, Questions, and Topics for Study

door life and scenery and ethical tales of poetic quality. This story is one of a collection entitled *The Unknown Quantity*. Other enjoyable volumes are *Fisherman's Luck*, *The Valley of Vision*, *Little Rivers*, *The First Christmas Tree*, and *The Story of the Other Wise Man*.

Pirie MacDonald
HENRY VAN DYKE

1. Tell this story, briefly, in your own words.

2. How may one lie without uttering a word? Give examples. Explain the saying, "His word is his bond."

3. Oliver Wendell Holmes said, "Satan has many tools, but a lie is a handle which fits them all." What does this mean?

4. How is a liar a coward? Give an example.

5. Successful homes, business, and governments must be founded on truth. Why?

6. How are sham, pretense, evasion, and living beyond one's means forms of lying?

Spinning Our Fates

William James (1842–1910) taught psychology at Harvard. His stimulating talks to students and teachers had a wide influence, not only in scientific lines but in the field of morals as well. He tried to lead his students to think for themselves, always expressing, in simple language, great truths about the psychical, physical, and moral natures.

1. Give, in your own words, the substance of this article.

2. How do we daily spin our fates, making ourselves fit, or unfit, to meet the Angel's Hour?

3. Give an account of the three Fates in whom the Greeks believed. •

4. "Great occasions do not make heroes or cowards. They simply unveil them to the eyes of men. Silently and imperceptibly, as we wake or sleep, we grow and wax strong, we grow and wax weak; and at last some crisis shows us what we have become." Can you cite occasions in actual life or in fiction that illustrate the truth of the foregoing passage?

What Is Liberty?

Woodrow Wilson (1856–1924), the war president, twenty-eighth holder of the presidential office, was born in Staunton, Virginia, shortly before the Civil War. He grew up in the rather strict atmosphere of a Presbyterian minister's household. After graduation from Princeton, he studied law at the University of Virginia.

He practiced law for some years. In 1910 he became president of Princeton University, and governor of New Jersey in 1911. In 1912 he was elected president of the United States, serving two strenuous terms, during which the great World War and the difficult adjustment of the questions involved in bringing about peace and right relations between the nations were a severe tax

Notes, Questions, and Topics for Study

upon his physical resources. Finally he succumbed to the fearful pressure, dying at his home in Washington. He is entombed there in the new Episcopal Cathedral.

Wilson's fine ideals of government relationships and high sense of civic duties and responsibilities are embodied in many books and in many eloquent speeches. This article is taken from a volume of speeches called *The New Freedom*.

Harris & Ewing

WOODROW WILSON

1. How did President Wilson answer the question, "What is liberty?"

2. Explain how fair play enters into business and civic relationships.

3. What did Wilson mean by the "New Freedom"? What did he expect of the United States? Why?

4. Our liberty ends when it conflicts with the liberty of another. Explain this statement, using your classroom as an illustration.

5. Why is coöperation necessary for success in the home? in the school? in the city or state?

Cadet Prayer

Officers for our army are trained at the United States Military Academy at West Point on the Hudson. Besides learning the art of war, the students, called

Appendix

cadets, are inspired, by the West Point tradition, to emulate the characters and deeds of former West Pointers, men like General Robert E. Lee, "Stonewall" Jackson, Albert Sidney Johnston, Ulysses S. Grant, and other Civil War leaders, as well as many leaders of the Great War, like Generals Pershing, Liggett, Bullard, and others. In this beautiful prayer, Chaplain Wheat

Wide World Photos

CADETS ON DRESS PARADE AT WEST POINT

has expressed the fine ideals which the West Point tradition includes.

1. Most unexpectedly is the soldier often called upon to face the Angel's Hour. Can you give some examples? How would this prayer help a man to face it successfully?

2. Why is it courageous to choose "the harder right"? Give some instances where men or women, boys or girls have thus chosen.

332

Notes, Questions, and Topics for Study

3. Explain how the honor of the corps would help to steady a man in a crisis. How can you help to build up a school tradition?

4. Do advantages of birth, of training, or of education confer obligation? Explain your idea.

5. Compare the ideals of the Military Academy and of the Naval Academy.

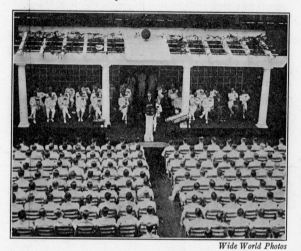

GRADUATION EXERCISES AT ANNAPOLIS

A Code of Citizenship

The United States Naval Academy, located at Annapolis, Maryland, was organized to train officers for our navy. The roll of our distinguished naval heroes from Dewey to the honor men of the last war, whose efficiency made possible our landing an army on foreign soil, is evidence of the high standard to which the midshipmen must subscribe and the vigorous training they must undergo.

In this selection is a statement of the code to which the academy subscribes.

1. What is a code? Do you know of other school or organization codes? Cite one you know.

2. What qualities are necessary for a good naval officer?

3. A western high school formulated the following code and urged every student, particularly every athlete, to examine himself to see whether he was a true sportsman. Comment on the code. Are there any additions or omissions that you would suggest?

A Good Sportsman:

Does not misrepresent his eligibility.

Will avoid unnecessary roughness that might injure an opponent.

Plays fairly at all times.

Plays his best to the end whether he is winning or losing.

Plays for the fun of playing and for the success of his team.

Regards visiting contestants as guests and treats them accordingly.

Is courteous to officials, accepts adverse decisions graciously and expects them to enforce rules.

Congratulates the winners, gives them full credit, does not explain or make excuses.

Is modest in victory; does not brag or "rub it in."

Observes training rules and seeks in all ways to represent his school worthily.

Among his fellows is fair, courteous, and determined. Above all, he is a gentleman.

4. Captain Scott was a naval officer. Name some American naval officers who were arctic explorers.

Notes, Questions, and Topics for Study

5. What are some of the essentials of a gentleman?

6. Over the New York Post Office is engraved: "Neither snow nor rain nor heat nor gloom of night stays these couriers from the swift completion of their appointed rounds."

On one of the Oxford colleges is engraved:

> He who reads and reads
> And does not what he knows
> Is he who plows and plows
> And never sows.

Explain these two inscriptions.

To His Daughter

William James (1842–1910) was not only a philosopher and a Harvard professor, but a kind and interested father who wrote charming and stimulating letters to his children. Just as he tried to make his students think for themselves, so he tried to lead his children to stand on their own feet both mentally and spiritually.

What was William James's remedy for a moody, melancholy state of mind?

To John D. Johnston

The life story of Abraham Lincoln (1809–1865) is one of the epics of American history. His pioneer childhood and youth laid the foundation stones of character on which he rose, step by step, until he became sixteenth president of the United States. This letter to his stepbrother exhibits the Lincoln traits of thrift, shrewd common sense, kindliness, humor, and frankness. The

Appendix

beautiful Lincoln Memorial, in Washington, is a national shrine, though his body was entombed at Springfield, Illinois.

1. How do you explain the moral failure of John D. Johnston?
2. Do you approve Lincoln's advice?

To His Son

Though we know and love Dickens (1812–1870) chiefly as the great novelist, yet he wrote charming and humorous letters to his friends and very delightful letters to his children. In this letter to his son he tells him some of the things which will help him to make right choices when he is faced with the necessity of reaching decisions.

State briefly in your own words the advice Dickens gave his son.

ADDITIONAL QUESTIONS AND SUGGESTIONS

1. An old man, crossing the street while it was snowing, did not see an approaching automobile. He was knocked senseless. The chauffeur sped away. What is your opinion of the chauffeur? If you had seen the accident, what would you have done?
2. A woman left her hand bag on the seat in a theater where she had been sitting. An usher found it after she had left the building. He was ignorant of the owner's whereabouts. What should he have done with the bag?
3. Two boys, tormenting a wretched-looking kitten,

Additional Questions and Suggestions

were noticed by some passers-by, none of whom stopped. What course would you take were you passing such a scene?

4. During the Christmas rush a post-office clerk gave a woman a dollar too much. The woman returned the dollar. What sort of woman do you think she is?

5. Thoughtless customers order unnecessary and trivial articles to be sent C. O. D. with small intention of keeping them. The goods are returned, giving sales people, chauffeurs, messengers, and clerks much trouble and causing expense which the general public must pay for. Discuss this custom and its influence on character.

6. Some boys, in what they called "fun," seized an automobile standing at the curb, drove it as far as the gasoline supply allowed, and then abandoned it. What do you think of this sort of fun? Their fathers had to replace the car. Was their fun worth its cost? Explain.

7. The family is going on a week's vacation in the car, and will camp at night. What shall be done with the refuse? What do you think of tourists who break off branches of laurel and dogwood? What do you think of people who uproot wild flowers or kill song birds?

8. A stranger asked Mary where the nearest subway station was. Mary gave her wrong directions so that the stranger lost her way and also lost an appointment with a prospective employer. Why is accuracy a useful trait? Have we a moral obligation to be accurate?

9. Do you boast of your clothes, your parents, your

home, your success in games, and things you have or do? When Helen was asked if she had a new dress, she boastfully answered that she had ten new dresses. How can one cure a boaster?

10. Do you know of any man or woman who turned a disability into an asset? How? Who was it? How was the change accomplished?

11. Cite instances in your school experience which served as the spear of Ithuriel in revealing true character.

12. William James, the educator, states as one of the fundamentals of democracy " that habit of trained and disciplined good temper toward the opposite party when it fairly wins its innings," in short, sportsmanship. Cite instances of sportsmanship that you have heard of in connection with school athletics.

13. Cite crucial instances in history in which the chief actors were called on to make ethical choices.

14. Perhaps you are familiar with the scales and tests by which we are able to rate ourselves in intelligence, in use of English, and in other subjects. Perhaps you would like to measure your progress in forming habits and attitudes of good citizenship. The *Chassell-Upton Citizenship Scales*, published by Teachers College, Columbia University, are recommended.

15. Using the words *high*, *average*, and *low*, rate yourself with reference to the following characteristics:

> Poise
> Initiative and originality
> Industry
> Persistence

Accuracy
Promptness
Honesty
Cheerfulness
Courtesy
Coöperation
Sense of fair play
School spirit
Sense of responsibility
Unselfishness
Strength as a leader
Ambition to know
Ambition to excel
Kindness
Tolerance of others' opinions
Mental ability

SUGGESTIONS FOR FURTHER READING

Following is a list of readings in prose and poetry, selected because the theme of each deals with some aspect of character. As you and your class read, make a brief comment on each one. Let your comment be concise and exact. Try to find other titles that could be added to the list.

Adams, Elmer C., and Warren D. Foster: *Heroines of Modern Progress*

Andrews, Mrs. M. R. S.: *Courage of the Commonplace*

Atkinson, Eleanor S.: *Greyfriars Bobby — Johnny Appleseed, the Romance of a Sower*

Appendix

Baldwin, James: *An American Book of Golden Deeds —
Fifty Famous Stories Retold*

Barrie, James M.: *Margaret Ogilvy Barrie*

Barton, Clara H.: *The Story of the Red Cross*

Bennett, Arnold: *How to Live on Twenty-Four Hours a
Day*

Birkhead, Alice: *Heroes of Modern Europe*

Black, Hugh: *Friendship*

Bolton, Sarah K.: *Lives of Girls Who Became Famous*

Bond, A. Russell: *Pick, Shovel, and Pluck*

Bridges, T. C., and H. H. Tiltman: *Heroes of Modern
Adventure*

Bunyan, John: *The Pilgrim's Progress*

Bush, Bertha E.: *Prairie Rose*

Camp Fire Girls: *The Book of the Camp Fire Girls*

Chute, Arthur Hunt: *The Mutiny of the Flying Spray*

Clarke, George Herbert: *A Treasury of War Poetry*

Coe, Fanny E.: *Heroes of Everyday Life*

Connor, Ralph: *Black Rock — The Sky Pilot*

Crump, Irving: *The Boys' Book of Arctic Explorations*

Darling, Esther B.: *Baldy of Nome*

Daudet, Alphonse: *Monsieur Seguin's Goat*

Davis, Richard Harding: *The Boy Scout, and Other
Stories*

Dawson, William James: *The Book of Courage*

Driggs, Laurence L.: *Heroes of Aviation*

Duncan, Norman: *Dr. Grenfell's Parish*

Eastman, Charles A.: *Indian Heroes and Great Chief-
tains*

Eaton, Walter Prichard: *The Boy Scouts at Crater Lake
— The Boy Scouts in Glacier Park*

Suggestions for Further Reading

Faris, John Thompson: *Winning Their Way*

Ferris, Helen, and Alice Mary Kimball: *Girl Scout Short Stories*

Forbush, William B.: *The Young Folks' Book of Ideals*

Fraser, Chelsea: *Heroes of the Air*

French, Henry W.: *The Lance of Kenana*

Gaston, Charles R. and Gertrude Fales: *Modern Lives*

Gilbert, Ariadne: *More than Conquerors*

Gilchrist, Beth B.: *The Life of Mary Lyon*

Girl Scouts: *Scouting for Girls* (official handbook)

Godfrey, Vincent H.: *John Holmes at Annapolis*

Golding, V.: *The Story of David Livingstone*

Grayson, David: *Adventures in Friendship — The Friendly Road*

Greene, F. N., and D. W. Kirk: *With Spurs of Gold*

Grenfell, Wilfred: *Adrift on an Ice-Pan*

Griswold, Lotta: *Deering of the Deal, or The Spirit of the School*

Hale, Edward E.: *Boys' Heroes*

Hammond, John Winthrop: *Magician of Science: The Boys' Life of Steinmetz*

Henley, William Ernest: *Lyra Heroica: A Book of Verse for Boys*

Hermans, Mabel C.: *Stories from the Old Testament*

Heyliger, William: *High Benton — Don Strong of the Wolf Patrol*

Hudson, W. H.: *Little Boy Lost*

Hughes, Thomas: *Tom Brown's School Days*

Hull, Eleanor: *The Boy's Cuchulain*

Humphrey, Grace: *Heroes of Liberty*

Jewett, Sarah Orne: *A Country Doctor — Betty Leicester*

341

Appendix

Jewett, Sophie: *God's Troubadour*

Keller, Helen: *The Story of My Life*

Kingsley, Charles: *Heroes*

Kipling, Rudyard: *Captains Courageous*

Lagerlöf, Selma: *The Christmas Guest — The Silver Mine*

Lang, Andrew: *True Story Book*

Lang, Mrs. L. B.: *The Red Book of Heroes*

Lanier, Henry W.: *A Book of Bravery*

Larcom, Lucy: *A New England Girlhood*

Lindbergh, Charles: *We*

Mabie, Hamilton Wright: *Heroines Every Child Should Know*

Maeterlinck, Maurice: *The Blue Bird*

Mathiews, Franklin K.: *Boy Scouts Courageous — The Boy Scout's Book of Camp Fire Stories*

Moffett, Cleveland: *Careers of Danger and Daring*

Moore, Mrs. N. Hudson: *Deeds of Daring Done by Girls*

Muir, John: *The Story of My Boyhood and Youth*

Mukerji, Dhan Gopal: *Gay-Neck, the Story of a Pigeon*

Neihardt, John G.: *The Song of Hugh Glass*

Newbolt, Henry: *The Book of the Happy Warrior*

Ollivant, Alfred: *Bob, Son of Battle*

Ouida (Louise de la Ramée): *A Dog of Flanders*

Page, T. N.: *Robert E. Lee, the Southerner*

Paget, Stephen: *I Wonder: Essays for Young People*

Paine, Ralph D.: *College Years*

Palmer, George Herbert: *Alice Freeman Palmer*

Parkman, Mary R.: *Heroes of Today — Heroines of Service*

Pyle, Howard: *Men of Iron — Otto of the Silver Hand*

Suggestions for Further Reading

Quiller-Couch, Arthur: *The Roll Call of Honor*
Richards, Laura E.: *Florence Nightingale*
Roosevelt, Theodore, and Henry Cabot Lodge: *Hero Tales from American History*
Shackleton, Ernest: *South!*
Shaw, Flora L.: *Castle Blair*
Singmaster, Elsie: *When Sarah Saved the Day*
Smith, Elva S.: *Heroines of History and Legend*
Smith, F. Hopkinson: *Tom Grogan — Caleb West*
Stefansson, Vilhjalmur: *My Life with the Eskimos — Hunters of the Great North*
Stevenson, Robert Louis: *Will o' the Mill*
Sweetser, Kate B.: *Ten Great Adventurers*
Tappan, Eva March: *American Hero Stories — Hero Stories of France*
Terhune, Albert P.: *Lad, a Dog*
Thomas, Lowell: *The Boys' Life of Colonel Lawrence*
Van Dyke, Henry: *The Blue Flower — The First Christmas Tree — The Story of the Other Wise Man*
Wallace, Dillon: *Grit-a-Plenty — The Long Labrador Trail — The Story of Grenfell of the Labrador*
Wiggin, Kate Douglas: *Polly Oliver's Problem*
Wildman, Edwin: *Famous Leaders of Industry*
Wyss, Johann David: *Swiss Family Robinson*
Yonge, C. M.: *A Book of Golden Deeds*